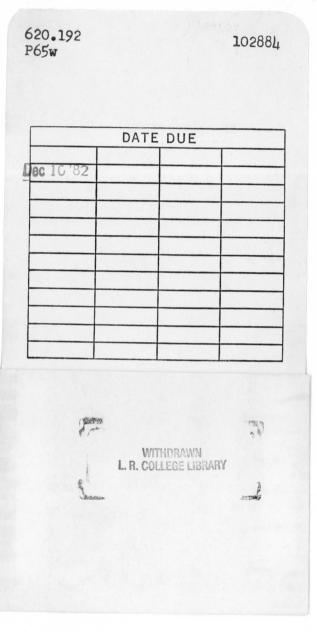

WEATHERING AND DEGRADATION OF PLASTICS

WEATHERING AND DEGRADATION OF PLASTICS

BASED ON
A SYMPOSIUM AT THE
BOROUGH POLYTECHNIC
LONDON

Edited by

S. H. PINNER

B.Sc., Ph.D., F.R.I.C., F.P.I.

GORDON AND BREACH, SCIENCE PUBLISHERS INC.

NEW YORK   LONDON   PARIS

©
1966 *by*
Columbine Press (Publishers) Ltd.

620.192
P65w
102884
Oct. 1977

Published by
GORDON AND BREACH
Science Publishers, Inc.
150 Fifth Avenue,
New York, N. Y. 10011

Library of Congress
Catalog Card No: 66-70078

Published in the United States of America
by Gordon and Breach, Science Publishers, Inc.
and in Great Britain by Columbine Press Ltd.

Printed in Great Britain at the Buxton Press

Foreword

PROBLEMS encountered in determining the factor responsible for the weathering and degradation of plastics in service provide a typical example of the fact that technology today is literally working at the frontiers of knowledge. The future development of plastics to meet a huge potential demand, particularly in the building industry, is essentially technological, but it is equally true that a satisfactory solution of the problems involved requires a more fundamental knowledge of the mechanisms of weathering and degradation processes. Already, a tremendous amount of scientific and technological research has been devoted to this end, but the knowledge acquired tends to be widely disseminated and much of it is not readily available.

It was for these reasons that the Borough Polytechnic, London, with its long experience of the value of advanced courses in various branches of science and technology, decided to organize a symposium specifically devoted to the weathering and degradation of plastics, and subsequently to make the proceedings of what proved to be a highly successful event available to a wider audience by the publication of the subject matter in the amplified, illustrated and fully documented form represented by this book.

Compiled by a team of authorities in their respective branches of polymer science and technology, and edited by Dr S. H. Pinner, an associate lecturer in the Department of Chemistry and Chemical Technology of the Borough Polytechnic, who organized the original symposium on which it is based, the book can confidently be recommended as providing a comprehensive assessment of existing knowledge on the weathering and degradation of plastics and constituting a progress report which should prove of the greatest value to all concerned with this important problem.

J. E. GARSIDE,
Principal, Borough Polytechnic,
London, S.E.1.

Contents

The Authors

A. AUSTIN
   BX Plastics Ltd., Manningtree, Essex.

H. C. BAILEY, PH.D.
   Distillers Co. Ltd., Epsom, Surrey.

W. I. BENGOUGH, B.SC., PH.D.
   Royal College of Science, Glasgow.

C. A. BRIGHTON, M.B.E., B.SC.
   British Geon, Barry, Glamorgan.

C. B. BUCKNALL, M.A.
   BX Plastics Ltd., Manningtree, Essex.

N. GRASSIE, B.SC., PH.D., D.SC., F.R.I.C.
   The University, Glasgow.

J. M. HEAPS, B.SC., PH.D.
   BX Plastics Ltd., Manningtree, Essex.

D. R. J. HILL, M.SC., PH.D.
   Borough Polytechnic, London.

W. G. SIMPSON, M.A.
   BX Plastics Ltd., Manningtree, Essex.

Editor

S. H. PINNER, B.SC., PH.D., F.R.I.C., F.P.I.
   *BX Plastics Ltd., Associate Lecturer in Polymer
   Science and Technology to the Borough Polytechnic.*

ix

Introduction

PRODUCTION AND CONSUMPTION of plastics have continued to rise at a phenomenal rate. Whereas consumption was less than half-a-million tons before the 1939 war, the current world consumption is estimated at near 10-million tons and some individual plastics are used at present in tonnages exceeding those of important non-ferrous metals. Even the rate of increase of production is increasing and there is no overt reason for this trend to change, considering the continuing rise in prime costs of traditional materials of construction. Accordingly, a further 20-fold increase in plastics consumption may occur before the end of this century.

Such huge quantities of plastics must be used in prominent applications not yet established, a major proportion of which will be external, in the course of which they will be exposed to the degradative influences of heat, ultra-violet light and atmospheric pollution. It follows that the degradation of plastics will be of great concern to future technologists and it was mainly for this reason that the subject was chosen for a Borough Polytechnic symposium and the decision subsequently made to publish the proceedings.

The arrangement of the book is systematic. The first chapter deals with the general chemical principles of oxidative, radiative and thermal degradation and this is followed by a chapter on experimental techniques for studying degradation phenomena. Plastics rely for weathering and thermal resistance to a great extent on the presence of small amounts of additives which are highly specific in their function and it is imperative to understand the chemistry of such additives. Accordingly, the unifying principles underlying the use of antioxidants, u.v. absorbers, antiozonants and heat stabilizers are discussed in Chapter 3.

One great difficulty in developing plastics with improved weathering performance is the relatively long time taken for these to break down when exposed outdoors. There is a great gulf between academic studies of polymer degradation and practical weathering trials, inadequately bridged by the range of accelerated tests in current use. There is need not only for more representative accelerated tests but also for some numerical correlations between the results of such tests and of outdoor exposure. Due to the vagaries of weather, such correlations are inordinately difficult but Chapter 4 suggests that reliable correlations can be achieved in special cases, though much background work must still be done.

After these generalized chapters, there are three chapters dealing specifically with the three major thermoplastic families; polyethylene, polyvinylchloride and polystyrene. Regrettably, coverage is incomplete; in a monograph on the degradation and weathering of plastics, it would be necessary to discuss many more families of plastics, but in practice only those mentioned above, together with polymethylmethacrylate, polyvinylfluoride and thermosetting resins such as phenol-formaldehyde and melamine-formaldehyde, are likely to find massive use under exposed conditions. Polymethylmethacrylate and polyvinylfluoride seem uniquely resistant to weathering and consequently little is published concerning their degradation during weathering. Little is known also about the breakdown of thermosetting resins, the behaviour of which under exposure is erratic, mostly good but sometimes failing after short periods due mainly to imperfect formulation and cure conditions.

In the form of surface coatings, polymers provide a line of defence against metallic corrosion, which costs this country many hundreds of millions of pounds per annum. Economies would result if the metal or wood were replaced by plastics and if the weathering resistance of the surface coating itself were improved. It becomes pertinent accordingly to refer to the weathering and degradation of plastics as "organic corrosion", though it must be remembered in applying this term that, while oxidative and hydrolytic influences are still at play, the mechanisms of breakdown of plastic and metal articles are entirely different. In the final chapter, the scope for weather-resistant plastics is discussed from an economic point of view and in relation to overall corrosion costs and projected building programmes.

There can be little doubt that, because of their ready availability, versatile properties and low cost, plastics will play an immense role in future building construction and that a knowledge of "organic corrosion" will be assuming ever greater importance. If the publication of this book merely advances a recognition of the problems, it will have achieved its purpose.

S. H. PINNER

CHAPTER I

Fundamental Chemistry of Polymer Degradation

by N. GRASSIE

THE FIRST IMPORTANT PUBLICATION concerned with the weathering of a commercial high polymer appeared in the Journal of the Chemical Society for 1861, when A. W. Hoffman reported upon his examination of the gutta percha covering of cable used in the construction of the East Indian telegraphs which had deteriorated rapidly after installation, involving substantial financial loss. Although the history of synthetic plastics is usually accepted as dating from the following year when Alexander Parkes presented his plasticized nitrocellulose, later known as *Parkesine*, at the Great International Exhibition, Hoffman's earlier work on the naturally occurring materials did illustrate a number of fundamental facts which are quite generally true of the modern synthetic plastics as well as of the naturally occurring high polymers. His work showed, for example, that deterioration could be associated with the absorption of oxygen and that it is accelerated by heat and also sometimes by light.

Modern interest in the weathering and degradation of plastics was originally concerned, however, with the stability of those few materials which were available commercially in the decade before the second world war. Emphasis was very much upon stabilization at that time and rule-of-thumb methods were often used in the choice of stabilizers, usually with very little understanding of their chemical action. This is not surprising, because the very existence of such large molecules was regarded more or less as a chemical curiosity at that time, and the deterioration problems associated with these new structural materials had to be solved as quickly and as cheaply as possible. What is surprising, however, is that this early interest did not stimulate industry into initiating or actively encouraging more research into the fundamental nature of polymer degradation, in recognition of the fact that only through a complete understanding of the fundamental chemistry of these processes would it be possible to plan fully effective measures for their prevention.

As more and more polymeric materials have become available and more extreme stability requirements have been demanded of them, interest in polymer degradation has broadened. Moreover, it has been recognized that fundamental information about the mechanisms of chemical changes in polymers under the influence of heat, visible and high energy radiation, oxidation, hydrolysis, etc., is essential if molecular structures resistant to these agencies are to be designed and synthesized. In consequence, the research work which followed has revealed a great deal of information regarding the relationships which exist between polymer structure and stability.

Many of the current problems of polymer degradation are considered in detail in subsequent chapters, and it is accordingly the function of this chapter merely to establish the general background and the connecting principles underlying degradation phenomena. Except, perhaps, to illustrate a general point, specific examples are not therefore discussed in great detail.

Degradative Agencies

While there is a large number of degradative agencies which may afflict polymeric materials, three are of particular importance in the application of polymers generally. These are (a) oxidation, (b) light and (c) heat, and as their action serves to illustrate the more important chemical features of polymer degradation, it is principally to the chemistry of reactions in polymers induced by these agencies to which this chapter is devoted.

Attention must be paid to degradation in two phases of the life of plastics. Firstly, during fabrication, in processes like moulding and extruding, materials are subjected to high temperatures in air. Consequently, thermal and oxidative degradation processes are often important. Secondly, during the subsequent useful life of the fabricated article, it is usually subjected more or less continuously to air and light, and oxidative and photodegradative processes are therefore most important. In special applications, high thermal stability may also be important, one example being in connection with polymers which are incorporated in light oils to produce viscostatic materials for use as engine oils and which will thus be subjected to elevated temperatures in use. Also, at the present time, a great deal of effort is being expended in creating high-temperature resistant synthetic materials, particularly for such applications as those associated with high-speed flight.

In any specific industrial or commercial application, it is often difficult to distinguish between the effects of these three agencies. More often than not, the overall deterioration of the material in question is the result of a composite process to which two or even all three contribute. Nevertheless, their respective functions in the overall deterioration process must be understood if the most effective steps possible are to be taken to stabilize the materials. It is clearly necessary, therefore, to separate these agencies and to investigate the chemical reactions which they can individually induce in polymers. Moreover, this approach has been stimulated by the intense academic interest which exists in the fundamental chemistry of these processes.

The Effect of Oxidation

From our knowledge of the sensitivity of carbon-carbon double bonds to attack by oxygen, it is not surprising to find that the unsaturated polymers are those most susceptible to oxidation. These include natural and the more common synthetic rubbers. The ultimate physical effects of such oxidation are well known; they are discolouration, hardening and surface crazing or, in more severe cases, actual surface cracking or flaking.

Polymer degradation reactions in general are difficult to put on a quantitative basis, and this is particularly the case with oxidation processes, partly because of the complexity of the products and the difficulties of analysis of functional groups attached to polymer chains, but also because the penetration of the oxygen into the material, and hence the rate of the reaction, so readily becomes diffusion controlled in all but the thinnest films.

It is for these reasons that polymer chemists first sought to elucidate the mechanism of the oxidation of relatively small molecules, which were used as models for segments of polymer chains, and to extrapolate the results of these experiments to polymers. The monumental work carried out by Bolland and his colleagues at the British Rubber Producers Research Association on unsaturated small molecules is now part of classical chemistry but it was only by this means that any clear idea could be obtained of the sort of processes going on in the oxidation of unsaturated rubbers.

The hydroperoxidation mechanism which they revealed is a radical chain process, the primary reaction steps of which are detailed overleaf:

Initiation   : Production of radicals (R˙)
Propagation : R˙ + O₂ → ROO˙
$$ROO˙ + RH → ROOH + R˙$$
Termination : R˙ + R˙ ⎫
$$ROO˙ + ROO˙ ⎬ \text{Inactive products}$$
R˙ + ROO˙ ⎭

RH is the parent compound, the hydrogen atom specified normally being the most reactive hydrogen atom in the molecule. R˙ is the radical formed by removal of this hydrogen atom, ROO˙ is the hydroperoxy radical formed by the addition of oxygen to it, and ROOH is the corresponding hydroperoxide.

In the model compounds which Bolland studied the chain length of this reaction is large. In other words, the propagation steps occur many times for each act of initiation and termination. This is also true in polymers when the molecules are relatively mobile, as in solution or at high temperatures. In polymers at ordinary temperatures, however, the molecules are relatively immobile and thus the second propagation step, which involves two polymeric entities, is inhibited and the chain length becomes very much shorter.

It is the reactivity of the hydrogen atoms, and hence the tendency for hydroperoxidation to proceed, which determines the susceptibility of any particular polymer to oxidation. Small concentrations of these hydroperoxides in themselves, however, do not affect very greatly the physical properties of the polymers. It is the subsequent reactions of these very unstable groups which cause discolouration, embrittlement, cracking, and other faults.

Hydroperoxides can decompose by scission of the oxygen-oxygen bond,

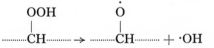

and since they are so unstable, this is a very potent source of radicals for the initiation of further oxidation.

These radicals may also react in pairs to produce cross-links, or decompose,

to give aldehydic or ketonic substances which are typically found in oxidized polymers.

It is also believed that a great deal of the cross-linking which causes embrittlement is due to reaction of the radicals with double bonds in the polymer structure.

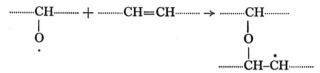

Unsaturated polymers are highly susceptible to oxidation because the double bonds activate α hydrogen atoms. In a segment of the natural rubber molecule, for example,

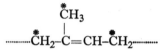

the carbon-hydrogen bonds marked with an asterisk are all more reactive than are similar bonds in a fully saturated structure. This allows them to take part more readily in the second propagation step of hydroperoxidation.

Although saturated polymers in general are more stable to oxidation, they are frequently seriously affected, particularly if they incorporate reactive hydrogen atoms. For example, the tertiary hydrogen atoms in polystyrene,

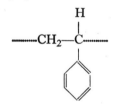

are sufficiently reactive to absorb a considerable amount of oxygen over a long period. The primary oxidation product is presumably the hydroperoxide

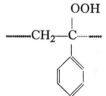

and it is the reactivity of these hydrogen atoms which has prevented the use of the very much cheaper polystyrene in place of polymethylmethacrylate as a transparent glass substitute when clarity over a long period is required. If unprotected by u.v. absorbers, polystyrene articles discolour quite seriously in outdoor conditions. In solid rigid polymers of this sort, oxidation is very much a surface reaction, being limited by the rate and depth of the diffusion of oxygen into the polymer.

Light Degradation

In the past, the influence of visible light radiation on the deteriorative weathering of commercial polymers has not always been fully appreciated. In the overall weathering process it is, indeed, often quite difficult to unravel photo and oxidative effects. As a result of recent fundamental investigations into polymer degradation, however, it seems that light can enter into the picture in a number of ways which may be generalized under the headings: (a) direct effects, (b) initiation of oxidation and (c) delayed effects.

DIRECT EFFECTS

When rubber, polystyrene and certain other polymers are irradiated in the absence of oxygen, hydrogen is produced and insolubility occurs due to cross-linking. This is referred to as the photogelation of rubber and is due to the following sequence of reactions:

$$RH \rightarrow R^{\cdot} + H^{\cdot}$$
$$R^{\cdot} + R^{\cdot} \rightarrow R-R \text{ (cross-linking)}$$
$$H^{\cdot} + H^{\cdot} \rightarrow H_2$$

In the case of rubber, it has even been possible to show that the number of cross-links is approximately equal to the number of molecules of hydrogen formed.

In general and as expected, this reaction occurs more readily the more reactive the hydrogen atoms which are removed. Hence the reason why it occurs so readily in rubber and polystyrene is because the radicals which are produced by the removal of the most reactive hydrogen atoms in these molecules are stabilized respectively by allylic and aromatic resonance,

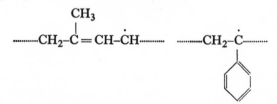

As shorter and shorter wave length and hence higher and higher energy radiation is used, polymers with less reactive hydrogen atoms behave in this way so that a wide variety can be gelled even by ultra-violet radiation.

With very high energy radiation, such as X-rays, γ-rays or electrons, relatively very unreactive hydrogen atoms can be removed as, for example, in polymethylmethacrylate.

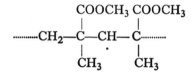

It is generally true, however, that the less reactive the hydrogen atoms removed, the more reactive, and thus the less stable, are the resulting radicals. In turn, the less stable the radicals, the more likely are they to decompose rather than to combine to give cross-links. Thus in polymethylmethacrylate, decomposition resulting in chain scission predominates,

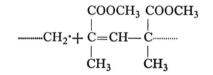

so that in such polymers the molecular weight decreases—the reverse of gelling.

It will be seen, therefore, that there is nothing fundamentally different between the action of high energy radiation, which for obvious reasons has created a great deal of interest in recent years, and that of visible light. Polymers which gel in light do so also under the influence of high energy radiation and for the same reason. Polymers unaffected by light undergo chain scission on exposure to high energy radiation because the same types of primarily formed radicals react in a different way.

INITIATION OF OXIDATION

It is quite clear that the radicals produced in polymers by light are precisely those which are involved in the hydroperoxidation process. This reveals the second major effect of light, namely as an initiator of oxidation. Often under atmospheric conditions it is found that oxidation occurs at the surface whereas deeper in the polymer mass photogelation occurs, the oxygen supply at these levels being limited by diffusion.

Delayed Effects
The delayed degradative effect of light is possibly best exemplified by polyvinylchloride. Thermal degradation of this polymer involves loss of hydrogen chloride. If one molecule of hydrogen chloride is liberated an unsaturated structure remains,

$$\cdots\cdots CH_2\text{--}CHCl\text{--}CH\text{=}CH\text{--}CH_2\text{--}CHCl\cdots\cdots$$

but this unsaturated centre, by creating allylic structures, activates the decomposition of the adjacent monomer unit so that the loss of hydrogen chloride passes from unit to unit along the chain.

Irradiation can apparently create such isolated unsaturated bonds in polyvinylchloride. The presence of a small proportion of these does not affect its appearance or physical properties significantly but they quite clearly constitute the seeds for its ultimate rapid deterioration.

The thermal discolouration of polystyrene is also activated in a dramatic way by prior irradiation. Thus polystyrene degraded thermally in vacuum remains colourless as it volatilizes at 320 °C. Preirradiated polystyrene, on the other hand, rapidly discolours through yellow and brown to black at very much lower temperatures. Clearly, irradiation has produced structures in the polymer which can initiate a new type of thermal reaction to which unirradiated material is immune.

Thermal Degradation

While oxidative and photo effects follow a well defined pattern in the sense that they are all closely associated with the reactivity of hydrogen atoms and the reactions of hydrocarbon type radicals, thermal degradation is concerned with a wide variety of reaction types and provides a diverse wealth of material for study. In addition, while oxidative and photo reactions proceed, at least qualitatively, in a manner to be expected by comparison with the behaviour of model compounds, thermal degradation studies are apt to hold many surprises.

Although one is sometimes tempted to doubt it, polymers do obey the fundamental laws of chemistry and thus, provided adequate information is available, reactions in polymers should always be explicable in terms of classical chemical behaviour. It is reasonable therefore to expect that the thermal behaviour of any given polymer should be predictable by comparison with the behaviour of model compounds. Thus, for example, polyethylene might be expected to have similar stability to a shorter chain paraffin like hexadecane, while polymethacrylate esters might be expected to decompose to olefin and acid like so many simple esters. Yet polyethylene shows signs of decomposition about 200° lower than does hexadecane, and while model primary esters give olefin and acid at about 450-500°C, polyethylmethacrylate gives an entirely different product-monomer at 200°C.

This lower thermal stability of polymers compared with model compounds is typical of polymers generally. The reasons are usually quite subtle but, speaking in the broadest terms, two main reasons can be found for the decrease in stability.

Firstly, to represent a polymer molecule as a large number of monomer units linked end-to-end as in

$$\cdots\cdots CH_2\text{--}CHCl\cdots\cdots \quad \text{or} \quad \text{--}(CH_2\text{--}CHCl)_n\text{--}$$

gives rather an idealized picture. The chain ends will be structurally different and, in addition, many polymers have irregularities in the body of the molecular chains. These structural abnormalities can have a profound effect, out of all proportion to their concentration, on the rate and sometimes even on the fundamental nature of the degradation reaction. Secondly, the polymer chain environment in which the reaction is taking place may modify the reaction. Often this occurs by converting a simple step-by-step reaction in the model into a chain reaction in the polymer. A few specific examples may be useful in illustrating these points.

Structural irregularities may appear in polymer molecules as the result of a relatively infrequent step occurring as an integral part of the polymerization process. For example, the limited but well defined decrease in molecular weight which occurs in the early stages of the thermal degradation of polymethacrylonitrile has been traced to the decomposition of labile ketene-imine groups which are present in the polymer as a result of the reaction during polymerization of the methacrylonitrile radical A, in its alternative canonical form B.

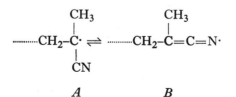

$$A \qquad\qquad B$$

Possibly the most common labile abnormalities built into polymer molecules during the polymerization process are those associated with unsaturation. When termination occurs by disproportionation of radicals during the polymerization of methylmethacrylate, for example,

$$\cdots\cdots CH_2-\underset{\underset{COOCH_3}{|}}{\overset{\overset{CH_3}{|}}{C}}\cdot \quad + \quad \underset{\underset{COOCH_3}{|}}{\overset{\overset{CH_3}{|}}{C}}\cdot-CH_2\cdots\cdots \quad \rightarrow \quad \cdots\cdots CH_2-\underset{\underset{COOCH_3}{|}}{\overset{\overset{CH_3}{|}}{CH}} \quad + \quad \underset{\underset{COOCH_3}{|}}{\overset{\overset{CH_3}{|}}{C}}=CH\cdots\cdots$$

or when transfer to monomer occurs during the polymerization of vinyl chloride,

$$\cdots\cdots CH_2-CHCl\cdot + CH_2{=}CHCl \rightarrow \cdots\cdots CH_2-CH_2Cl + CH_2{=}CCl\cdot$$

$$CH_2{=}CCl\cdot + monomer \rightarrow CH_2{=}CCl-CH_2-CHCl\cdots\cdots$$

the bonds in α positions with respect to the double bonds will be relatively more reactive by reason of the allylic nature of the resulting radicals. Thus thermally induced radical processes are most likely to be initiated at these points. The thermal depolymerization of polymethylmethacrylate has been shown to be initiated at such chain ends and the strong tendency for polyvinylchloride to lose hydrogen chloride and become discoloured is almost certainly due, at least partially, to the ready initiation of the reaction at these points.

Chain branches, which are also formed during the polymerization process, have also been held in part responsible for the instability of polyvinylchloride and are certainly points of potential instability in polyethylene.

There are in polystyrene a limited number of weak links distributed apparently at random in the molecules. Their decomposition on heating causes chain scission and a consequent sharp fall in molecular weight. Although they have not been identified positively, a good deal of evidence about them has been revealed. Thus they are formed in a reaction which competes directly with the propagation step during polymerization. They are neither chain branches nor head-to-head linkages but they are associated with unsaturation in the polymer chain backbone since the same decrease in molecular weight as occurs thermally at high temperature can be induced to occur by ozonization at low temperature. On the basis of evidence of this kind, the chemical nature of these weak links has been speculated upon, the most plausible proposal being that they may result from reaction of the polystyryl radical in an alternative canonical form, such as *C*.

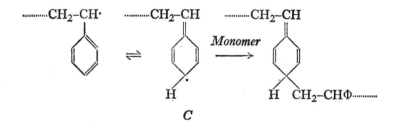

C

Impurities which have become incorporated into polymer molecules may also act as labile structural abnormalities. For example, methacrylic acid, which can appear in methacrylonitrile by monomer hydrolysis and which will ultimately appear in the polymer chains by copolymerization, is an extremely efficient initiator for the internal nitrile group polymerization which causes rapid discoloration of the polymer owing to the conjugation which is introduced.

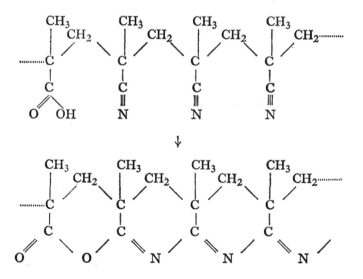

Similarly, traces of certain monomers, acrylonitrile in particular, introduced into polymethylmethacrylate by copolymerization, cause rapid chain scission at temperatures lower than that at which thermal degradation normally occurs in the pure homopolymer.

Numerous examples may also be cited to illustrate effects which the polymer chain environment may have when a reaction in a polymer is compared with that in a model.

The course of the ester decomposition reaction in polyvinylacetate, for example, is largely determined by the fact that it is occurring in a long linear molecule. The molecular mechanism by which carboxylic acid esters decompose to acid and olefin is facilitated by the six-membered ring interaction which can clearly exist between the β-hydrogen atom of the alcohol residue and the carboxyl group.

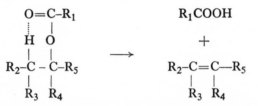

The tendency for the β-hydrogen atom to be attracted to the oxygen atom will be enhanced by electron-attracting substituents in the positions $R_2 - R_5$. Thus the tendency in polyvinylacetate for adjacent units to react to produce conjugation and colour can be explained in terms of the electron-attracting properties of the carbon-carbon double bond activating the adjacent methylene group:

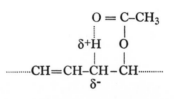

Thus the liberation of acetic acid from polyvinylacetate and the accompanying coloration is a molecular chain reaction in which initiation consists of the loss of a molecule of acetic acid from a saturated chain. The double bond so formed facilitates loss of an adjacent acid molecule which is the propagation step. Such a process is clearly entirely dependent upon the reaction occurring in a polymer chain environment.

Quantitative ester decomposition also occurs in polytertbutylmethacrylate except that in this case the olefinic product, isobutene, is liberated and the acid constituent, methacrylic acid, remains bound in the polymer chain. In this case too, the residue from units which have decomposed is found to accelerate the decomposition of adjacent units.

As in polyvinylacetate, a direct chemical mechanism has been suggested to explain the effect but it is of interest that an alternative purely physical steric effect has also been proposed. There must be considerable steric interference between adjacent tert-butyl groups in the polymer chains which must inhibit, to a large extent, free roations about the bonds in these groups. Thus in intact chains, the β-hydrogen atoms may be effectively held out of contact with the carbonyl oxygen atoms with which they must interact for ester decomposition to occur.

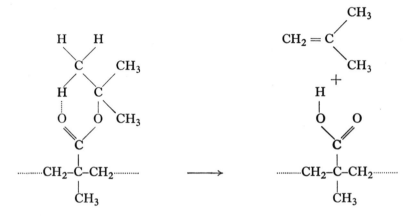

Replacement of an ester by an acid unit might release the steric strain to such an extent that this interaction is facilitated.

BIBLIOGRAPHY

1. "Polymer Degradation Mechanisms". *U.S. Natl. Bur. Stand. Circ.*, 525, 1953.
2. H. H. G. Jellinek, "Degradation of Vinyl Polymers", Academic Press, New York, 1955.
3. N. Grassie, "The Chemistry of High Polymer Degradation Processes". Butterworths, London, 1956.
4. "Thermal Degradation of Polymers", *S.C.I. Monograph*, No. 13, 1961.

CHAPTER 2

Experimental Techniques
for Studying Degradation

by D. R. J. HILL

As INDICATED IN THE PREVIOUS CHAPTER, the most important degradative agencies which afflict plastics are heat, light and oxygen, and to these may be added, moisture. Degradation also occurs in machines under mechanical shear which, in the extreme, might be termed mastication. Shear-induced degradation, however, lies outside the scope of this work and its discussion will not therefore be considered.

It is important to recognize that the polymerization of unsaturated monomers to chain polymers is a reversible process. Given an initiator, the reaction proceeds spontaneously at normal or somewhat elevated temperatures, with liberation of excess energy as heat, but as the temperature rises, the depolymerization becomes relatively important and under certain conditions an equilibrium may be reached. Accordingly, the effect of heat on many addition polymers is merely to undo the polymerization. Thus polymethylmethacrylate simply yields the monomer on pyrolysis and this property has been used in commercial plants for production of methylmethacrylate. For such polymers, depropagation is an inherent property of the polymer molecule and will proceed at a theoretically calculable rate, given a source of initiation of the depropagation reaction. In other cases, the degradation reaction is more complicated and less amenable to theoretical interpretation.

The effects of constituent groupings, weak links and environment having been discussed in Chapter I, it is necessary here to consider the experimental techniques which have been developed to demonstrate the response of plastics in general to degradative agencies. Since the purpose of such studies varies in particular cases, it is convenient to classify the methods into three groups, *viz.*, (*a*) studies of serviceability, (*b*) depropagation studies and (*c*) elucidation of degradation mechanisms.

Normal service tests often lead to an indication of the mechanism of degradation, but their main purpose is to ascertain the resistance of the plastic towards exposure. Depropagation studies are principally of value for conveying an understanding of the inherent response of the particular polymer structure. A combination of the former groups of test allows theoretical predictions of the degradation mechanisms to be verified or disproved. Attention is normally focussed in such studies on (*i*) the chemical nature of both volatile products and residue, (*ii*) the change in polymer molecular weight with depropagation, and (*iii*) the change in the rate of reaction with depropagation.

After outlining the most common test methods, some examples of the results are given so as to bring out the power of experimental techniques for illustrating degradative tendencies of plastics and aiding development of more degradation and weather-resistant varieties.

Thermodynamic Stability

For any chemical reaction to take place, two requirements must be satisfied: (*i*) it must be thermodynamically feasible and (*ii*) there must be a path for the reaction to proceed at a measurable rate. High molecular weight polyformaldehyde provides an example where depropagation is thermodynamically feasible at room temperature. In the absence of a reaction path, however, the polymer is quite stable at normal and elevated temperatures. If active end groups are formed, for example by exposure to ionizing radiation, then depropagation will proceed at a measurable rate at room temperature.

In a normal addition polymerization reaction—for example, the conversion of styrene to polystyrene—since the polymerization is a reversible reaction, the overall reaction rate R_p is not k_p [M·] [M] as usually written but strictly:

$$R_p = (k_p [M] - k_d) [M·] \qquad \cdots \qquad \cdots \qquad \cdots \quad (1)$$

Moreover: $\overline{DP}_n = (k_p [M] - k_d) [M·] / f [M·] \qquad \cdots \qquad \cdots \quad (2)$

instead of $\quad \overline{DP}_n = k_p [M] [M·] / f [M·]$

where $f [M·]$ is a complex function of [M·], the monomer radical concentration.

As the temperature rises, the depolymerization reaction becomes more and more important and when the polymerization and depolymerization reaction rates become identical, equilibrium has been reached[1]. The temperature at which this equilibrium occurs is called the ceiling temperature T_c as shown in Fig. 1 for styrene polymerization. In Fig. 2 are shown the variations which may be expected for the particular cases of catalyzed (E_i finite)* and radiation-induced ($E_i \sim$ zero) reactions with and without chain transfer. X is the limiting slope of the rate of propagation against tempera-

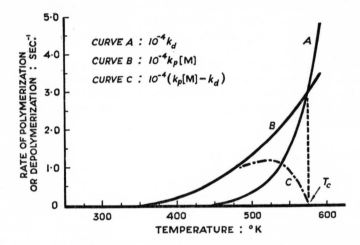

FIG. 1. VARIATION IN POLYMERIZATION AND DEPOLYMERIZATION
REACTION RATES OF STYRENE WITH TEMPERATURE

ture at the ceiling temperature. These curves show that the type of mechanism in operation controls the shape of the curves and that as well as R_p becoming zero, $\overline{DP}_n$ falls continuously with temperature in all cases.

It is obvious from these figures that the study of the change of reaction rate or $\overline{DP}_n$ with temperature leads to the value of T_c.

It can be shown in fact that

$$\lim_{T \to T_c} (d\,R_p/dT) = k_p\,[M]\,[M\cdot]\,\Delta H_p/RT_c^2 \qquad \ldots \qquad \ldots \qquad (3)$$

where k_p [M] [M·] is the rate which would have been observed at T_c in the absence of depropagation. In Fig. 2, T_c is found by extrapolation.

---

* E_i is energy of activation for initiation.

The slope of line X gives $\lim\limits_{T \to T_c} \left(\dfrac{dR_p}{dT} \right)$ and so ΔH_p can be readily calculated. These values agree with those determined by conventional calorimetry.

It can also be shown that

$$T_c = \Delta H_p / \left(\Delta S_p^\circ + R\ln[M] \right) \quad \ldots \qquad \ldots \qquad \ldots \qquad \ldots \quad (4)$$

where ΔS_p° is the entropy change for $[M] = 1$ mole litre^{-1}. Thus

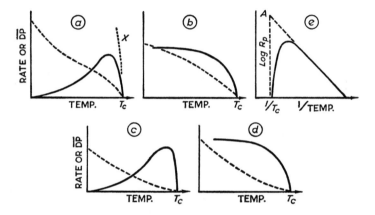

FIG. 2. EXPECTED SHAPES OF RATE-TEMPERATURE (FULL LINES) AND DP-TEMPERATURE (BROKEN LINES) GRAPHS, WITHOUT TRANSFER (UPPER THREE) AND WITH TRANSFER (LOWER TWO) TO MONOMER.

In graphs a, c, and e, E_i is finite
In graphs b and d, $E_i \frown$ zero

if ΔH_p is determined either by the above method or by calorimetry, and the monomer concentration is known in equilibrium with polymer at some temperature in "the region of balance", then ΔS_p° can be determined.

To establish a reasonably mobile equilibrium between monomer and polymer, it is necessary for a minimal concentration of active centres to be present throughout. For systems in which there is no termination, e.g., for α-methylstyrene catalyzed by sodium naphthalene in tetrahydrofuran, active centres are always present and equilibrium is therefore attained rapidly. Usually, however, active centres are lost by termination processes and it is then necessary to balance this loss by continuously supplying fresh active centres through an initiation reaction of either monomer or polymer. Even so, the approach to equilibrium is rather slow[2], as exemplified by Fig. 3 which shows the approach to equilibrium of methylmethacrylate in o-dichlorobenzene solution using photo-chemically generated active centres. This slowness makes it advisable to extrapolate to obtain the value of T_c. Fig. 4, which deals with the photochemically-induced equilibrium between gaseous methyl methacrylate and its solid polymer[3], shows there is no

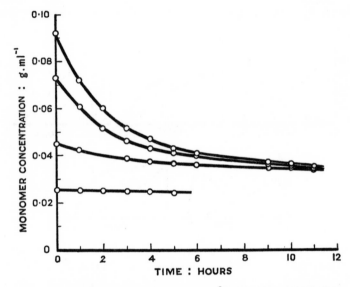

FIG. 3. EFFECT OF TIME AT 132·2°C ON THE MONOMER CONCENTRATION OF METHYLMETHACRYLATE (PHOTO-SENSITIZED BY THE SOLVENT O-DICHLOROBENZENE)

unique value for T_c, as this depends on the value of [M]. The temperature at which the rate of production or loss of monomer is zero is the ceiling temperature for the particular monomer concentration and pressure.

If reaction rates are available at various temperatures, ΔH_p need not be determined separately, as ΔH_p and ΔS_p° can be obtained from the slope and intercept of a plot of ln [M] against $1/T_c$.

It is possible, of course, to obtain entropy values from specific heat measurements on the monomer and polymer by application of the third law of thermodynamics, although a difficulty arises in that polymers seldom approach perfect crystallinity at absolute zero. However, the residual entropy is probably seldom in excess of 1 cal. deg.$^{-1}$ mol^{-1} and the few determinations which have been carried out by this method are quantitatively significant.

When experimental values of ΔH_p and ΔS_p° are not available, it is sometimes possible to make estimates by means of a semi-empirical group method such as that of Anderson, Beyer and Watson[4]. These methods depend upon the experimental fact that

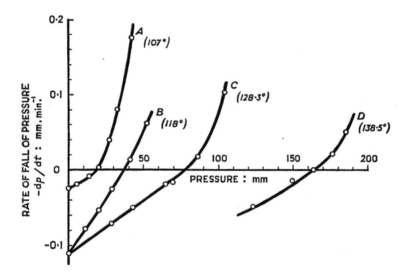

FIG. 4. RATE OF FALL OF PRESSURE ON IRRADIATION OF A
MIXTURE OF GASEOUS METHYLMETHACRYLATE WITH ITS
SOLID POLYMER AT VARIOUS TEMPERATURES

The field above the pressure axis corresponds to
polymerization and that below to depolymerization

thermodynamic properties are approximately additive, introduction of a given group into different compounds having the same effect so long as the substitution is made at a structurally similar point.

Such calculations have led to a close understanding of the relationship between polymer degradation products and monomer and polymer structure. It is found that the value of ΔH_p for a polymer is a useful index of stability. Polymers which give high monomer yields on thermal degradation are those with low $-\Delta H_p$, e.g., polyformaldehyde, polymethylmethacrylate and polymethyl-styrene. In many cases, the depropagation reaction may have to compete with hydrogen abstraction and other reactions, especially for polymers for which $-\Delta H_p$ is relatively high, *e.g.*, polyethylene, polyacrylonitrile and polyvinylacetate.

Thus, thermodynamic studies give vital information regarding polymer stability and enable one to predict the general mechanistic behaviour. However, specific breakdown mechanisms are often complex and can only be fully understood by employing experiments specially designed to unravel degradation mechanisms.

Classification of Methods

Studies of serviceability involve such questions as whether given plastics are likely to be stable in use and to what extent processing conditions, or the presence of plasticizers, antioxidants, stabilizers, etc., affect the heat-resistance or weather-resistance of the product. For these purposes, two types of weathering test—natural weathering tests and accelerated weathering tests—have been evolved. The former requires the samples, after suitable preparation and conditioning, to be placed in an exposed site usually facing south at an angle of $45°$ to the horizontal plane for varying periods up to 20 years. Periodically, the samples are removed, reconditioned and visually inspected or mechanically tested. Accelerated tests are employed to reduce the time-scale and enable information on the durability of a plastic to be received in time to make modifications to process or composition. Accelerated tests are more useful for testing experimental materials, while natural aging tests are more reliable for drawing up specifications for established products. Procedures in both categories have been accepted by the American Society for Testing and Materials and these are summarized below.

Variations from the standard technique are described in the literature for testing the heat-resistance of plastics. Most of these still prescribe a standard period of conditioning and a standard physical or mechanical test method after the exposure. Often a preliminary series of experiments is described, the purpose of which is to determine the approximate rapid failure temperature for a short exposure, failure being defined as some specified change in appearance, light transmission, weight, length, flexural or impact strength or other properties. A test might then be carried out for a longer period such as seven days at $30°C$ below the approximate rapid failure temperature. Subsequently, exposure temperatures are changed incrementally to arrive at the precise maximum service temperature. Frequently, such tests involve exposure of the samples not only to heat but also to u.v. light, corrosive gases or other aggressive agencies. There has been a great increase in such testing recently in pursuit of ablation-resistant plastics for use in satellites or supersonic aircraft.

Depropagation studies normally require the use of pyrolysis equipment. Polymer samples are generally heated under desired conditions and provision made for the collection of volatile products. Most commonly, high vacuum is applied, and sometimes the arrangement is that of a molecular still, allowing separation of various fractions within the apparatus. Where u.v. irradiation is needed to maintain a supply of active centres, part of the exposure tube is made of quartz or Vicor glass to allow penetration of u.v. light. Volatile products may be trapped by cooling or may be absorbed by specific liquid absorbents. The latter are necessary when acid or alkaline gases are evolved as in the degradation of nylon[5] or chlorine-containing polymers[6].

The detailed study of degradation mechanisms requires more sophisticated equipment, often specifically designed to give the required information. Mass spectrography, gas chromatography and infra-red and ultra-violet spectroscopy are powerful techniques widely used to identify volatile products. It is often desired to examine also the solid residue from pyrolysis and this can be rather more difficult, but chemical changes can still be determined chemically or by infra-red and u.v. spectral analysis and, if the polymer remains soluble, its molecular weight as well as other solution properties can be determined. This information is most revealing of mechanism, in contrast with physical or mechanical test results on the polymer residue, which are difficult to relate to chemical change. Techniques which allow continuous monitoring of the rate of degradation as a function of the amount and chemical nature of volatile products or residue are particularly valuable.

Accelerated and Natural Weathering Tests

A standard accelerated weathering test is described in ASTM D795-57T and requires the sample to be exposed alternately to u.v. light and fog. The samples rotate on a gramophone turntable (at 33 r.p.m.) while exposed to an S-1 u.v. lamp which is placed so as to raise the temperature to 55-60 °C, as registered on a thermometer lying with its bulb at the turntable centre. The fog chamber consists of a closed shallow box fitted with a spraying unit and a baffle to prevent the spray from impinging directly on the specimens. The distilled water spray should deposit a fine mist on the specimens without washing action. Radiation and wetting cycles for each 24-hour period are as follows: two hours in the fog box, two hours irradiation, two hours in the fog box and 18 hours irradiation; many other cycles are used in practice. The u.v. intensity can be checked by means of a colour scale test or a uranyl oxalate actinometer. The former employs coloured (*e.g.*, blue or grey) cloths which begin to fade after different times of exposure, dependent on the incident intensity. In the latter case, the solution changes chemically in direct proportion to the amount of u.v. light received. Such u.v. intensity assessment tests are also useful in the

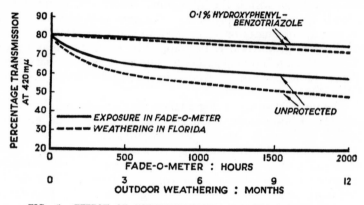

FIG. 5. EFFECT OF HYDROXYPHENYL BENZOTRIAZOLE AS A STABILIZER ON THE LIGHT ABSORPTION OF POLYESTER SHEET AFTER BOTH NATURAL AND ACCELERATED WEATHERING

operation of a Fade-O-Meter, which is a chamber used for the u.v. and visible light irradiation of polymer samples.

The related natural weathering test method (ASTM 1435-58) is very wide in scope and merely requires the conditioned sample to be exposed at an angle of 45° facing south and then tested after desired periods. Fig. 5 shows typical results from a natural and accelerated weathering experiment, designed to measure the protection against weathering conferred upon polyester sheets by 0·1 per cent hydroxyphenyl benzotriazole[7], while Fig. 6 shows that the required absorber concentration can be obtained by such accelerated tests. Wallder and associates[8] considered 100 hours exposure of polyethylene to a bare carbon arc under prescribed conditions to be equivalent to one year of exposure outdoors. For a given material and a steady climate, it seems reasonable to attempt such correlations. Other examples of attempted correlations between outdoor and accelerated weathering are referred to in Chapter 4.

Thermal Degradation Studies

A typical apparatus for carrying out thermal degradation studies[9] is shown in Fig. 7, in which A represents the sample vessel, a borosilicate glass tube fitting into a larger borosilicate glass tube B. A sample weighing about 20-50 mg. is outgassed in vacuo at 100-150°C and placed in the tube A at D^1, and the system is evacuated to 10^{-5}—10^{-6} mm. A tube furnace wound with nichrome wire is first preheated to the required experimental

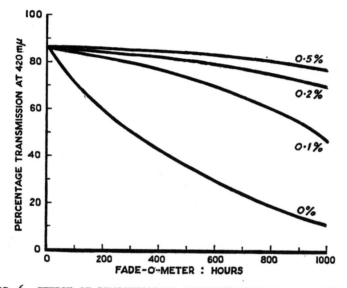

FIG. 6. EFFECT OF BENZOTRIAZOLE CONCENTRATION ON THE LIGHT
ABSORPTION OF SPARINGLY INFLAMMABLE POLYESTER SHEETS
SUBJECTED TO ACCELERATED WEATHERING

temperature as measured by the platinum-rhodium thermocouple D and moved into position around B. After a prescribed time of heating, often 30 minutes, the furnace is removed.

The following fractions may be collected:

(1) Residue: Not volatile at the temperature of pyrolysis.
(2) Fraction V_{pyr}: Volatile at the temperature of pyrolysis.
(3) Fraction V_{25}: Volatile at 25°C but not at –80°C.
(4) Fraction V_{-80}: Volatile at –80°C but not at –190°C.
(5) Fraction V_{-190}: Volatile at –190°C.

During pyrolysis, stopcock E is kept closed. The volatiles condensable at −190 °C remain in the system and are condensed in a liquid nitrogen trap F. Any part of the volatiles not condensable at −190 °C. are moved to the left of stopcock G by a mercury diffusion pump H.

At the end of pyrolysis, stopcock G is closed and the pressure of the non-condensable gas is measured by the McLeod gauge, a sample of this gas being sealed off in tube I at point J for analysis in the mass spectrometer. From a knowledge of the volume of the apparatus between G and E, the total weight of this fraction V_{-190} can be calculated.

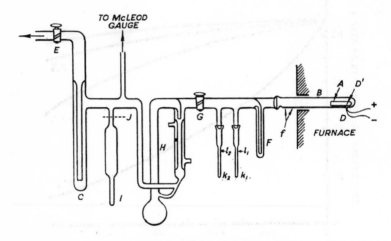

FIG. 7. APPARATUS FOR THE PYROLYSIS OF POLYMERS AND THE PARTIAL FRACTIONATION OF PRODUCTS

The condensate in trap F is separated into two fractions V_{-80} and V_{25} by normal distillation and trapping methods. After sealing tubes K_1 and K_2, the contents are analyzed in the mass spectrometer.

Fraction V_{pyr}, volatile at the temperature of pyrolysis but not at room temperature, condenses inside tube B at f. It is collected by dissolving in benzene and its weight is measured after evaporating the solution in a weighed platinum crucible. The weight of residue not volatile at the temperature of pyrolysis is obtained by direct weighing of tube A.

Fractions V_{-190}, V_{-80} and V_{25} are normally readily analyzed by mass spectrometry. Fraction V_{pyr} usually has an average molecular weight of several hundred and cryoscopic and infra-red and ultra-violet spectral techniques can sometimes be used to analyze this fraction and the residue.

When pure addition polymers are subjected to vacuum pyrolysis, the composition of the pyrolyzate is most distinctive. As shown in Table 1, polymethylmethacrylate and poly-α-methylstyrene undergo virtually complete reconversion to monomer, while polyethylene and polyisoprene yield larger fragments, due to a chain transfer step competing with depropagation.

TABLE 1.
PROPORTION OF MONOMER RESULTING FROM THERMAL DEGRADATION

Polymer	Per Cent Monomer Weight	Mole
Polymethylmethacrylate	100	100
Poly-α-methylstyrene	100	100
Polyisobutylene	32	78
Polystyrene	42	65
Polybutadiene	14	57
S.B.R. (Butadiene-styrene copolymer) ...	12	52
Polyisoprene	11	44
Polyethylene	3	21

Polyvinylacetate and polyvinylchloride, not shown in the table, yield largely acetic acid and hydrogen chloride, respectively, together with a coloured, unsaturated, high-polymeric residue. This is interpreted as a side-chain degradation mechanism, the side chain bonds being weaker than the main chain bonds.

Still further information concerning the degradation mechanism of such polymers as polymethylmethacrylate can be obtained by arresting the reaction before complete pyrolysis and measuring the molecular weight of the residue by viscometry or osmometry [10]. Fig. 8 shows a typical series of results on polymethylmethacrylate. Examination of these curves gives much information regarding the mechanism of degradation, the average length of depolymerization run or the zip length, the frequency of transfer and so on. When the curves lie below the diagonal, another mechanism involving the breaking of weak chain bonds is indicated. When curves closely follow the ordinate scale, indicating gradual molecular reduction without production of monomer, a mechanism of random bond scission without chain depolymerization is also indicated.

Such studies require the estimation by conventional methods, usually based on osmotic pressure or viscometry, of the number-average molecular weight of the residue at various stages of a polymer pyrolysis. For polymers with a normal molecular weight distribution, simple formulae exist to relate $\overline{DP}_v$ and $\overline{DP}_w$ to $\overline{DP}_n$

and so viscometry or light scattering methods can also be used to obtain the required $\overline{DP}_n$.

Often, curves are constructed of the ratio M/M_0 against the percentage of volatiles and not the percentage of monomer. In such cases the term L has to be introduced, L being the number of carbon atoms in the species just too large to volatilize.

The percentage breakdown to monomer or volatiles can be determined by simple weighing or chemical analysis.

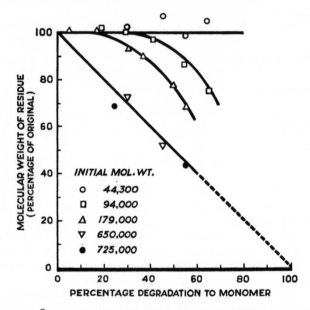

FIG. 8.   CHANGE IN THE RELATIVE NUMBER-AVERAGE MOLECULAR WEIGHT OF POLYMETHYLMETHACRYLATE ON DEGRADATION TO MONOMER

Some curves showing the change in the rate of reaction with amount of degradation are given in Fig. 9. The shape of these theoretical curves is governed by the type of initiation, the zip length*, the type of termination and related factors[11]. When experimental curves are encountered resembling a certain theoretical curve, an immediate clue to the breakdown mechanism arises. Similarly in oxidation, particular mechanisms lead to characteristic

* The zip length refers to the number of successive monomer units lost from the chain following initial scission.

curves of oxygen absorption rate as a function of the total oxygen absorbed. Adherence to such characteristic curves can be taken as indicative of the particular mechanism. A number of techniques, in particular thermogravimetric analysis and differential thermal analysis, allow continuous measurement of chemical change over a fixed time interval or a predetermined temperature cycle and the

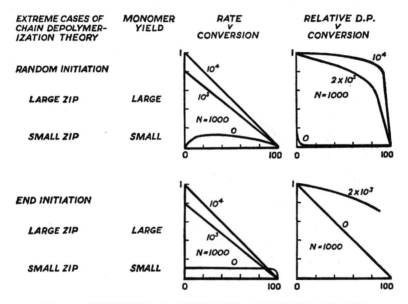

FIG. 9. COMPARISON OF THEORETICAL RESULTS FOR EXTREME
CASES OF THE DEPOLYMERIZATION THEORY

Values of zip [1/e—1] are given above the curves.
Rate scales for rate curves with zero zip are multi-
plied by a factor of 100 for random initiation and
by a factor of 50 for end initiation

results of such measurements lend themselves well to mechanistic interpretation.

Elaborate equipment is not always required for thermal degradation studies. Andrianov[12] obtained useful information about the stability of polymeric siloxanes relative to some organic poly-mers by heating 1-10g. samples in a furnace under an inert gas stream or in vacuo and weighing intermittently. Some of his results for degradation at 350°C are shown in Fig. 10.

This work can be rendered far less laborious by suspending the polymer sample on a spring balance. Madorsky[13] used this technique extensively to weigh samples continuously while undergoing pyrolysis under high vacuum. A typical balance used in thermogravimetric analysis is illustrated in Fig. 11. The spring is normally made from annealed tungsten wire, the crucible from platinum and the crossline from phosphor bronze. This is fixed to the tungsten tension wire by means of hard Apiezon wax and the

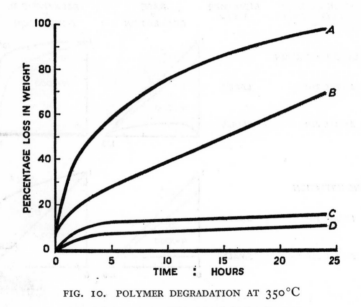

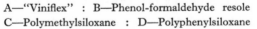

FIG. 10. POLYMER DEGRADATION AT 350°C

A—"Viniflex" : B—Phenol-formaldehyde resole
C—Polymethylsiloxane : D—Polyphenylsiloxane

extension is obtained by measuring the position of the crossline relative to a scale with a cathetometer.

More recently, recording microbalances such as the Stanton TRI thermobalance have become available. The furnace temperature and sample weight are simultaneously displayed on a twin-pen electronic recorder. The temperature can be raised at a linear rate to 1,000°C or held constant at any temperature up to this maximum. The sample is contained in a shallow silica crucible mounted on a silica rod connected to one pan of an analytical balance. The furnace is mounted vertically above the sample and can be lowered over it. A typical thermogravimetric curve as obtained by Heron[14] using the Stanton balance is shown in Fig. 12.

Interpretation of such non-isothermal curves is somewhat specialized and usually involves characterization of pyrolysis by two principal parameters, the "integral procedural decomposition

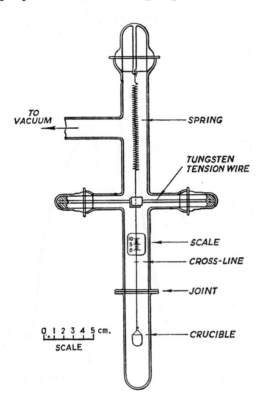

FIG. 11. TUNGSTEN SPRING BALANCE FOR
POLYMER PYROLYSIS STUDIES

temperature" T_p, and the procedural activation energy E_p, according to the proposals of Doyle[15] and Newkirk[16]. T_p describes the onset of weight loss, while E_p is calculated from the change of slope of weight loss with temperature.

Instead of weighing the residue continuously, a record of the progress of the reaction can be obtained by collecting the gaseous decomposition product in a confined volume and noting the pressure rise or, alternatively, by restricting the flow of vapour to the pump by making it pass through a narrow orifice and measuring the steady state pressure in the pyrolysis chamber. The pressure upstream from the orifice will be determined by the rate of production of vapour. When dealing with polymethylmethacrylate, the vapour composition is constant and the pressure produced by the orifice is proportional to the rate of loss in weight of the polymeric

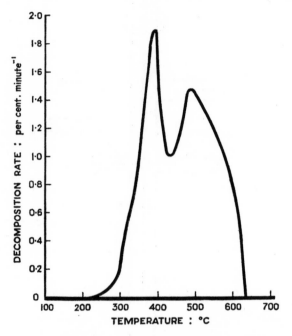

FIG. 12.   DERIVATIVE THERMOGRAVIMETRIC CURVE OF
PHENOLIC RESIN HEATED IN AIR

residue. It is convenient to measure the pressure by a Pirani gauge or by a thermocouple gauge coupled to a recorder.

Miscellaneous Methods

Differential thermal analysis allows irregular heat flow patterns in a substance to be studied in an environment in which the temperature is changing, This method is particularly apt for determining whether a substance undergoes exothermic and/or endothermic reactions during the course of heating. Two similar samples mounted side-by-side in a furnace are linked by thermo-couples, one sample being a blank compound such as alumina which will undergo no reactions, the other being the polymer. If the polymer sample undergoes no reaction, the recorder trace will be a straight base line throughout a heating programme. Any chemical reactions or phase changes will give peaks. The method is capable of giving useful information as to specific reactions occurring in polymers over a wide temperature range, especially if carried out in support of other methods. The possibilities of this method have been reviewed by Murphy[17] and others [18, 19].

Nuclear magnetic resonance (NMR) is mainly of help for elucidation of the structural and physical features of polymers and has not been used thus far in degradation studies. Electron spin resonance (ESR), however, offers a method for the elucidation of chemical processes and is more useful in this context. Most of the ESR studies on polymers have been concerned with materials after their exposure to atomic radiation. Such exposure leads to forma-tion of polymer radicals which are easily trapped at room temper-ature and have lifetimes of months or even years. In thermal degradation, the concentration of radicals is very small at the high temperature of the experiment and it has not been possible to identify any specific radical species occurring in degradation pro-cesses. It is a method, however, which offers very great possibilities in the future [20, 21].

Model compounds of high polymers have been used in many studies because they facilitate the analysis of chemical changes. For example, great insight was given into the auto-oxidation mech-anism of the degradation of unsaturated polymers, such as natural rubber, by the study by Bolland[22] of the rates of oxygen absorption of ethyl linoleate. The apparatus employed in these experiments is shown in Fig. 13.

During an oxidation run, an automatic device was employed to maintain the oxygen pressure at the selected standard value, the consumption of oxygen with time being measured by the burette. From curves of the rate of oxygen absorption against the total amount of O_2 absorbed, detailed and satisfactory mechanisms were formulated.

In studies of the thermal embrittlement of nylon, Harding and MacNulty[23] showed that the surface molecular weight dropped after exposure to high temperature while the interior increased in molecular weight and sometimes gelled. Eight aromatic amines were examined for their ability to protect nylon from degradation. From the relationship between the elongation at break or the tensile strength and the molecular weight of the surface layer of the nylon mouldings, sensible proposals were put forward as to the chemical reactions involved in nylon degradation.

Additives were also used by Grieveson, Haward and Wright[24] who studied the thermal oxidation of high density polyethylenes

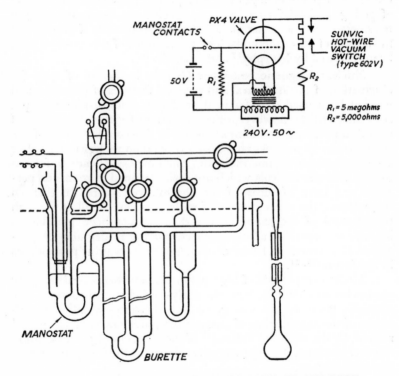

FIG. 13. APPARATUS FOR MEASURING RATES OF OXIDATION, TOGETHER WITH THE CIRCUIT OF THE ELECTRONIC RELAY

and related the length of the induction period to the antioxidant concentration. Results followed the simple relation:

$$T - T_0 = K\,[AH]^n$$

where T = induction time, T_0 = induction time for unstabilized polymer and $[AH]$ = antioxidant concentration. The oxidation rate varied with temperature in accordance with the Arrhenius relation.

Induction times are quite frequently observed during service-type weathering and heat stability tests.

An unusual technique is that of Andrianov[12] who obtained valuable quantitative data from tests of thermoelasticity. The thermoelasticity of films was determined on copper and aluminium supports. A film was considered to have lost its elasticity when, after being heated, it gave cracks on bending at room

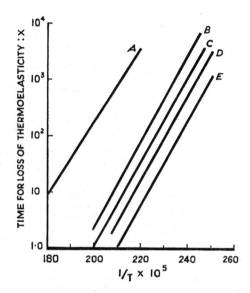

FIG. 14. EFFECT OF TEMPERATURE ON THE
TIME FOR LOSS OF THERMOELASTICITY

A : Polydimethylphenylsiloxane
B : Polyester of terephthalic acid with glycol and glycerol
C : Polyester epoxide
D : Polyester of sebacic acid with glycol and glycerol
E : Polyvinylformalethylol

temperature around a rod 3 mm. in diameter. The cracking point was taken to imply a uniform degree of chemical change and the rate of the reaction was taken to be inversely proportional to the time to crack. Satisfactory Arrhenius plots were obtained, as shown in Fig. 14, where X represents the times for the loss of thermoelasticity. Activation energies were calculated and agreed well with those calculated from the fall in breakdown voltage on aging.

Reference may finally be made to the classical work on the

thermodynamics and kinetic theory of rubber elasticity which makes it easier to relate changes in mechanical behaviour to chemical changes in elastomers. By combining continuous and intermittent stress relaxation measurements, Tobolsky and collaborators[25] have unravelled the competing processes of cross-linking and chain scission which are responsible for stress relaxation and creep.

REFERENCES

1. F. S. Dainton and K. Ivin, *Quart. Rev.*, 1958, **12**, 61.
2. S. Bywater, *Trans. Faraday Soc.*, 1955, **51**, 1267.
3. K. Ivin, *Trans. Faraday Soc.*, 1955, **51**, 1273.
4. J. W. Anderson, G. H. Beyer and K. M. Watson, *Natl. Petroleum News*, 1944, **36**, R476.
5. B. Kamerbeek, G. H. Kroes and W. Grolle, *S.C.I. Monograph, No.* **13**, 1961, 357.
6. A.S.T.M. D793-49.
7. H. Gusling and H. J. Heller, *Kunststoffe*, 1961, **51**, 13.
8. V. T. Wallder, W. J. Clarke, J. B. de Coste and J. B. Howard. *Ind. Eng. Chem.*, 1950, **42**, 2320.
9. S. Straus and S. L. Madorsky, *Ind. Eng. Chem.*, 1956, **48**, 1212.
10. P. R. E. J. Cowley and H. W. Melville, *Proc. Roy. Soc.*, 1952, **A210**, 461; 1952, **A211**, 320. N. Grassie and H. W. Melville, *Proc. Roy. Soc.*, 1949, **A199**, 1.
11. L. A. Wall and R. E. Florin, *J. Res. Nat. Bur. Stand.*, 1958, **60**, 451.
12. K. A. Andrianov, *S.C.I. Monograph, No.* 13, 1961, 75.
13. S. L. Madorsky, *Rev. Sci. Instr.*, 1950, **21**, 393.
14. G. F. Heron, *S.C.I. Monograph, No.* 13, 1961, 475.
15. C. D. Doyle, *J. Appl. Polymer Sci.*, 1961, **5**, 285, C. D. Doyle, *Anal. Chem.*, 1961, **33**, 77.
16. A. E. Newkirk, *Anal. Chem.*, 1960, **32**, 1558.
17. C. B. Murphy, *Anal. Chem.*, 1958, **30**, 867; 1962, **34**, 298R.
18. W. J. Smothers and Y. Chiang, "Differential Thermal Analysis, Theory and Practice". Chemical Publishing Co., New York, 1958.
19. J. B. Nelson, *Brit. Coal Utilisation Research Association, Monthly Bulletin*, 1955, **19**, 501-531.
20. Z. Frait, *Czechoslav. J. Phys.*, 1957, **7**, 577.
21. A. Tkac and V. Kellö, *Trans. Faraday Soc.*, 1959, **55**, 1211.
22. J. L. Bolland, *Proc. Roy. Soc.*, 1946, **A186**, 218.
23. G. W. Harding and B. J. MacNulty, *S.C.I. Monograph, No.* 13, 1961, 392.
24. B. M. Grieveson, R. N. Haward and B. Wright, *S.C.I. Monograph, No.* 13, 1961, 413.
25. A. V. Tobolsky, D. J. Metz and R. B. Mesrobian, *J. Amer. Chem. Soc.*, 1950, **72**, 1942. A. V. Tobolsky, I. B. Prettyman and J. H. Dillon, *J. Appl. Phys.*, 1944, **15**, 380. A. V. Tobolsky and R. D. Andrews, *J. Chem. Phys.*, 1945, **13**, 3.

CHAPTER 3

Chemistry of Antioxidants, Antiozonants and Heat Stabilizers

by H. C. BAILEY

MOST PLASTICS during their processing or in their normal lifetime are exposed to conditions which favour photo or thermal degradation and atmospheric attack by oxygen or ozone. The fundamental chemistry of polymer degradation has already been discussed in Chapter 1, but to enable the mode of action of the variety of stabilizers offered by modern technology to be fully understood, a brief re-examination of the mechanisms of oxidation and degradation will not be out of place.

The Mechanism of Oxidation

The oxidation of polymers by molecular oxygen is in most instances a free radical chain reaction, consisting of initiation, propagation and termination processes.

Initiation: Three initiating reactions are relevant to the problem of stabilization:

(*a*) If a polymer or its additives absorb u.v. light, there is the possibility of free radicals being formed by photo dissociation; for example,

$$RCOR \xrightarrow{h\nu} RCO\cdot + R\cdot \quad \dots \quad \dots \quad \dots \quad \dots \quad R.1$$

(*b*) The initial product of oxidation is usually peroxidic and capable of thermal dissociation to free radicals:

$$ROOH \rightarrow RO\cdot + OH\cdot \quad \dots \quad \dots \quad \dots \quad \dots \quad \dots \quad R.2$$

Catalyst residues from a free radical polymerization process will behave similarly.

(c) Hydroperoxides can be decomposed catalytically by metals of variable valency in redox reactions that produce free radicals at a rate greater than by thermal dissociation.

$$ROOH + M \rightarrow RO\cdot + OH^- + M^+ \quad \ldots \quad \ldots \quad \ldots \quad R.3$$

$$ROOH + M^+ \rightarrow ROO\cdot + H^+ + M \quad \ldots \quad \ldots \quad \ldots \quad R.4$$

The free radicals produced by these reactions, or by the shearing of polymer molecules during processing, attack the polymer to produce a new radical which, by reaction with oxygen, yields the peroxy radicals which propagate oxidation.

Propagation: Polymers, such as polyolefins, containing hydrogen atoms that can readily be removed by free radicals yield a hydroperoxide as the primary product of oxidation

$$ROO\cdot + RH \rightarrow ROOH + R\cdot \quad \ldots \quad \ldots \quad \ldots \quad \ldots \quad R.5$$

Conjugated olefinic groups can add peroxy radicals at the double bond[1].

$$ROO\cdot + -CH{=}CH{-}CH{=}CH{-} \rightarrow -\overset{\cdot}{C}H{-}CH{=}CH{-}CH{-} \quad R.6$$
$$\underset{OOR}{|}$$

1,5-dienes, such as polyisoprene, oxidize to both hydroperoxide and cyclic peroxide groups[2]

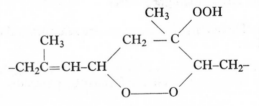

the latter being the probable sites of oxidative chain scission in the rubber molecule.

Olefins can also oxidize to epoxides in up to 50 per cent yield[3]

$$ROO\cdot + {>}C{=}C{<} \rightarrow RO\cdot + {>}C{-}C{<} \quad \ldots \quad \ldots \quad R.7$$
$$\underset{O}{\diagdown\diagup}$$

Termination: In all the above cases, the normal termination in air at atmospheric pressure is the reaction of pairs of peroxy radicals to form molecular products.

ANTIOXIDANTS

Antioxidants can usefully be described as interfering either with the initiation or propagation of oxidation; suppression of either will drastically reduce the rate of oxidation. In some instances a stabilizer may function in both capacities.

Agents suppressing Initiation

These agents fall into three groups, namely u.v. absorbers, peroxide deactivators and metal deactivators.

U.V. Absorbers: The most widely used compounds, the 2-hydroxy-benzophenones, are capable of absorbing u.v. light and disposing of the energy harmlessly without the formation of free radicals. This activity is related to the strength of the hydrogen bond formed in the chelate ring[4]

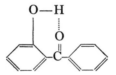

Similar compounds such as phenyl salicylates and resorcinol mono-benzoates probably undergo photo rearrangement to give 2-hydroxybenzophenones as the active stabilizers[5].

The 2-(2-hydroxyphenyl)benzotriazoles also contain an intramolecular ring system which probably facilitates the disposal of absorbed energy as in the hydroxybenzophenones. Substituted acrylonitrile light stabilizers contain no aromatic hydroxyl group, although their absorption in the near u.v seems to result from an aromatic substituent. Like the previous classes of compound, however, the substituted acrylonitriles presumably have some means of disposing of the absorbed energy without dissociating to free radicals. Metal phenates may in addition function as quenchers by deactivating electronically excited groups produced in the polymer by physical processes[6].

Where transparency is not required, pigments like carbon black give very effective protection against light.

Peroxide Deactivators: The function of these additives, which are mainly compounds of phosphorus and sulphur[7], is to cause a rapid decomposition of peroxides, principally hydroperoxides, before they dissociate to free radicals. While sulphides[8], organic phosphites[9] and phosphines[10] directly reduce hydroperoxides to alcohols, *e.g.*,

$$R_3P + ROOH \rightarrow R_3PO + ROH \qquad \dots \qquad \dots \qquad \dots \qquad R.8$$

catalytic reduction of the peroxides would lead to a longer lifetime for the antioxidant. Phenothiazine and other sulphur and phosphorus compounds have indeed been shown to bring about a catalytic decomposition of an aliphatic hydroperoxide and of cumene hydroperoxide to phenol[11, 12], these reactions probably being ionic.

Bateman and co-workers[13] have studied the behaviour of various sulphoxides and thiolsulphinates, which may be formed during the oxidation of sulphur vulcanised rubber, in the autoxidation at 75 °C of squalene, a 1,5-diene. They found that while these compounds do decompose the hydroperoxide, their principal effect is to complex with and drastically reduce the rate of homolytic decomposition of the hydroperoxide. In general, the hydroperoxides of olefins decompose to free radicals at a greater rate than do those of saturated compounds, probably because of an interaction between the olefinic and hydroperoxy groups. The breaking of this interaction by a more powerful complexing group for hydroperoxy groups may well increase the stability of the olefin hydroperoxides in the direction of that of secondary and tertiary alkyl hydroperoxides. This complexing action is very structure-sensitive; thus of a number of ketosulphoxides studied, those with the structure $RSOCH_2CH_2COR$ were found to be the most active. This confirms an earlier observation that among the ketosulphides, which were the precursors of the sulphoxides, the β carbonyl sulphides were the most effective antioxidants[14]. The well-known esters of thiodipropionic acid belong to this group. Substances such as thiolsulphinates have low thermal stability; but on decomposition they seem to give rise to products which are themselves powerful inhibitors[15].

Metal Deactivators: Metal deactivators function by co-ordinating with metals and altering their redox potentials so that the catalytic cycle R.3, R.4 is interrupted. They also block the formation of the complexes of metal and hydroperoxide which precede decomposition of the latter[16]. Donor compounds may be formed, as with the organic phosphines and phosphites, or chelate rings, as with bis-salicylidene diamines, hydroxy acids, oxamides and hydroxy or mercapto heterocyclics. The mere formation of a metal chelate is no guarantee of deactivation. The redox potential may be shifted in the direction of a more rapid reaction of metal with hydroper-oxide, thus disalicylidene ethylenediamine deactivates copper but further activates iron and cobalt in the oxidation of cyclohexene[17].

Propagation Suppressors

The best known antioxidants in this class are the phenols and aromatic secondary amines. It now seems well established that the phenols act by donating the hydroxyl hydrogen atom to peroxy radicals, leaving a stabilized radical which does not propagate further oxidation.

A substantial kinetic deuterium isotope effect[18] has been demonstrated in the oxidation of styrene initiated with azo-bis-isobutyronitrile and inhibited by 2,6-di-t.butyl-4-methylphenol (26B4M). Smaller isotope effects have also been reported for amine antioxidants[19,20]. The growth and decay curves of the phenoxy radicals formed during the oxidation of polypropylene films con-taining α or β naphthol have been measured by ESR techniques[21]. With amines, the ESR data are more difficult to relate to the in-hibition process as some amines readily form oxide radicals, such as diphenyl nitric oxide, by the reaction [19,22],

$$ROO\cdot + Ph\overset{\cdot}{N}Ph \rightarrow RO\cdot + Ph_2NO\cdot$$

The effect of structure on the reactivity of antioxidants has been described in three reviews[7,23,24] which cover the literature up to the end of 1961. Since then, a good linear relation has been demonstrated between the rate of reaction of styryl peroxy radicals with phenols substituted in the meta and para positions and electrophilic substituent constants[25].

Structural effects have been most widely explored in the case of phenolic antioxidants. In general they have been found to behave towards the attacking peroxy radicals as nucleophilic reagents; electron donors such as alkyl and alkoxy groups increase their activity while electron withdrawing groups decrease it.

More subtle effects of structure have been demonstrated by Bickell and Kooyman[26], who studied the effect of a number of phenols on the initiated oxidation of 9,10-dihydroanthracene. This hydrocarbon oxidizes very readily and the phenols retard oxidation rather than produce dead-stop induction periods. Two main types of behaviour were observed; phenols with heavily hindered hydroxy groups gave rates which were inversely proportional to the concentration of antioxidant, whereas with less hindered com-pounds, pronounced minima were observed, beyond which further increase of antioxidant concentration actually accelerated oxidation. Similar work in the laboratories of the Distillers Co. Ltd. fully confirms these observations, as illustrated by Fig. 15, which gives results obtained with the hindered phenol 26B4M and with di-o-cresylolpropane.

The kinetic scheme derived by Bickell and Kooyman gives a convincing interpretation of these results in terms of the observa-

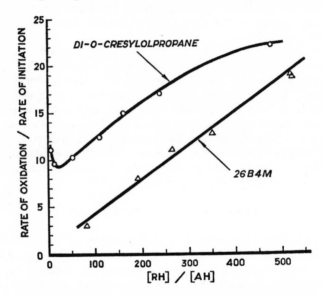

FIG. 15. RETARDING EFFECT OF THE HINDERED PHENOL 26B4M AND DI-O-CRESYLOLPROPANE ON THE OXIDATION OF 9:10 DIHYDROANTHRACENE

tion originally made by Bolland and t'en Have[27] that the radicals formed by hydrogen abstraction from an antioxidant might themselves abstract hydrogen from the hydrocarbon, this being a transfer reaction. For an initiator that dissociates to two free radicals, the reactions are as follows:

$$I \xrightarrow{k_i} 2R\cdot \to 2ROO\cdot \qquad \text{initiation} \qquad R_i$$

$$ROO\cdot + RH \xrightarrow{k_5} ROOH + R\cdot \qquad \text{propagation} \qquad R.5$$

$$ROO\cdot + AH \xrightarrow{k_8} ROOH + A\cdot \qquad \text{inhibition} \qquad R.8$$

$$A\cdot + RH \overset{k_9}{\to} AH + R\cdot \qquad\qquad \text{transfer} \qquad \text{R.9}$$

$$A\cdot + ROO\cdot \overset{k_{10}}{\to} ROOA \qquad\qquad \text{termination} \qquad \text{R.10}$$

With strongly hindered phenols, the transfer reaction is sterically inhibited, k_9 is zero and the rate of oxidation is given by:

$$-\frac{d[O_2]}{dt} = 2k_i I \left\{ 1 + \frac{k_5 [RH]}{2k_8 [AH]} \right\}$$

The ratio $2k_8/k_5$ is called the antioxidant efficiency and from the data of Fig. 15 is found to have the value 29 for 26B4M in dihydroanthracene at 60°C., compared with Kooyman's value of 33·5. The sum of R.8 and R.10 for 26B4M is:

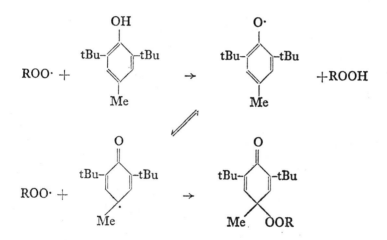

Two peroxy radicals are destroyed by the inhibitor and the product is a 2 or 4-peroxycyclohexadienone, which at low temperatures can be isolated in high yield[28,29].

If transfer occurs readily, the rate equation becomes

$$-\frac{d[O_2]}{dt} = 2k_i I + \left\{ k_5[RH] + k_8[AH] \right\} [RH]^{\frac{1}{2}} [AH]^{-\frac{1}{2}} \left(\frac{2k_i I k_9}{k_8 k_{10}} \right)^{\frac{1}{2}}$$

At constant initiator and hydrocarbon concentration, this simplifies to

$$\left(-\frac{d[O_2]}{dt} - 2k_i I \right) [AH]^{\frac{1}{2}} = C_1 + C_2 [AH]$$

This expression is plotted for di-o-cresylolpropane in Fig. 16 and gives a line from which the slope and intercept yield an antioxidant efficiency of 18·5 per hydroxyl group. For three alkylated p-cresols, the efficiencies[26] were found to be:

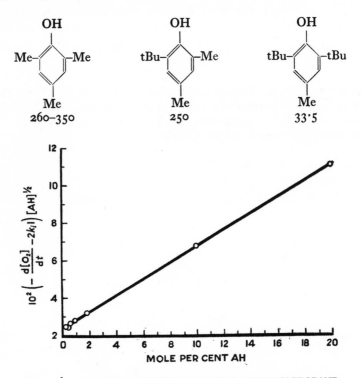

FIG. 16.   TRANSFER BEHAVIOUR OF DI-O-CRESYLOLPROPANE

Of these compounds only 2,4,6-trimethylphenol underwent transfer. Thus as hindrance of the hydroxyl group increases, the rate of reaction with peroxy radicals falls. This has recently been demonstrated[30] in a more technical application. Tests on a series of 2-t.butyl-4-methyl-6-aralkylphenols in various rubbers showed that as hindrance in the 6-position increased in the series

benzyl < methylbenzyl < dimethylbenzyl

the retarding effect on the autoxidation of the rubbers decreased. Steric hindrance also reduces the rate of the transfer reaction of phenoxy radicals with hydrocarbons. The practical effectiveness of a given antioxidant depends on the balance struck between the rates of the inhibition and transfer reactions. Many commercial phenolic antioxidants have a 2-t.butyl substituent, while the 6-substituent may vary from t.alkyl to hydrocarbon groups giving less hindrance.

The transfer reaction R.9 may be expected to require energy of activation, particularly for materials with strong C-H bonds, and will become relatively more important with increasing temperature. With di-β-napthyl-p-phenylenediamine in polyethylene, a maximum induction period at about 0·1 per cent by weight of additive developed as the temperature of the oxidation was raised above 160°C[31]. The effect has been more widely explored by Angert and Kuzminskii[32], who studied the oxidation of rubbers retarded by amine antioxidants. They found minimum rates which became more pronounced on progressing through the series ββ'-dinaphthylamine, phenyl-β-naphthylamine, diphenylamine, i.e., as hindrance of the secondary amino group decreased. With phenyl-β-naphthylamine, the concentration at which the minimum occurred was also found to depend on the structure of the rubber being oxidized, as the transfer equation predicts.

Shelton[20] has suggested that the pro-oxidant effect of some inhibitors when used at high concentrations is due to their direct reaction with oxygen to produce free radicals

$$AH + O_2 \rightarrow A\cdot + HO_2\cdot \quad \ldots \quad \ldots \quad \ldots \quad \ldots \quad \ldots \quad R.11$$

but this is unlikely to be of significance at low temperatures and the transfer seems quite adequate to explain such phenomena.

Synergistic Antioxidant Systems

Many multicomponent stabilizer systems for polymers have been described, particularly in the patent literature, which confer more protection against oxidation than the sum of the stabilizing actions of the components used separately. The probable mode of action in most cases is that they suppress both the initiation and propagation of oxidation. Since the propagation reaction produces peroxides which are potential initiators, while propagation can only follow initiation, the suppression of one reaction aids suppression of the other and synergism results. Typical binary combinations are phenols with peroxide destroyers, metal deactivators or u.v. stabilizers. Some antioxidants can themselves play a dual role; thus phenothiazine destroys both peroxides and peroxy radicals, while phosphites (phosphonates) can both co-ordinate with metals and reduce hydroperoxides.

Another possible mechanism in some binary stabilizer combinations is that one component serves to regenerate the other as the first is converted to an inactive form[33]. Evidence has been given recently that the cyclohexadienone peroxides formed from phenols on oxidation can be reduced back to the phenols by dilaurylthiodipropionate[34] which is often used as a co-stabilizer in polyolefins.

New synergistic systems for polyethylene have been described by Hawkins and Winslow[35]. Carbon black, frequently used as a reinforcing agent or light screen in plastics, reduces the reactivity of many phenolic or amine antioxidants. Oxygen-containing carbon blacks are themselves weak antioxidants but form very active synergistic systems when mixed with a variety of sulphur compounds, some of which have no activity on their own. The ability to form these highly active combinations with sulphur compounds was subsequently found to extend to soluble highly conjugated molecules such as polyacenes and quinones. Two mechanisms suggested for this behaviour are that the sulphur component may regenerate active phenol groups present in carbon blacks or that propagating free radicals produce thiyl $RS\cdot$ radicals by transfer with the sulphur compound, and these radicals are subsequently complexed by the conjugated component.

ANTIOZONANTS

Ozone is a very effective oxidation catalyst and will increase the rate of oxidation of most materials. On olefinic substances such as rubber, however, ozone has a more specifically damaging effect. The double bonds form ozonides which may rearrange with scission of the molecule[36]. Ozone is an electrophilic reagent and, therefore, its rate of reaction with a double bond increases if that bond is substituted with electron donor groups; the converse applies for electron acceptors. Polychloroprene is thus chemically more inert to ozone than polyisoprene.

Physical factors also play a major part in ozone cracking; damage is slight unless a critical minimum stress is exceeded, permitting surface rupture and the access of ozone; there is thus an energy requirement for serious damage to occur[37]. The growth of cracks is slow in materials of high internal viscosity but increases if these materials are plasticized or heated.

Antiozonants have been described as falling into two classes[38], (*a*) those which reduce the rate of crack growth, which includes a number of organic acids, amines, dihydroquinolines and zinc dialkyl dithiocarbamates, and (*b*) those which, in addition, cause large increases in the critical energy required for the propagation of cracks. This latter class, the substituted *p*-phenylenediamines, is of the greater technical importance. They are active antioxidants but an investigation of a series of substituted *p*-phenylenediamines indicated that their order of activity as antiozonants was the inverse of that as antioxidants, a maximum being reached in the *N*-alkyl-*N'*-aryl derivatives[39].

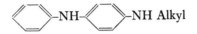

It seems unlikely that the scavenging of ozone plays much part in the activity of these materials, rather it has been suggested that these bifunctional materials react with the products of ozone scission, repairing the scission and producing a hardened surface layer[40].

HEAT STABILIZERS

Some polymers undergo specific elimination reactions on heating. Although these degradations are usually aggravated by oxygen, and can partially be controlled by antioxidants, they may also proceed in vacuo. The best known of these polymers is polyvinylchloride, which eliminates hydrochloric acid.

A wide range of stabilizers is in use, major groups being[41] (*i*) lead salts and soaps, (*ii*) salts and soaps of the group IIA and IIB metals, (*iii*) organo tin compounds, and (*iv*) high molecular weight epoxides. Various synergistic mixtures are also used.

When the degradation of polyvinylchloride was thought to be autocatalyzed by the hydrochloric acid evolved, a simple explanation of the action of these stabilizers was that they prevented such catalysis by absorbing HCl. All the above stabilizers do absorb HCl and this is probably of importance in preventing attack on processing machinery, with consequent generation of active degradation catalysts such as ferric chloride.

Conjugated unsaturation, of a chain length sufficient to absorb visible light, builds up at very low extents of HCl loss. The stabilization of polyvinylchloride is primarily a matter of suppressing this colour formation, which becomes objectionable before there is any substantial change in the physical properties of the polymer.

The γ-ray induced decomposition of polyvinylchloride at low temperatures is known to produce free radicals which lose HCl to form conjugated structures. The ESR absorption of these radicals can instantly be quenched by known radical traps such as nitric oxide and nitrogen dioxide[42]. Some recent patents[43,44] disclose these substances as stabilizers for polyvinylchloride and it is a reasonable assumption that they are also preventing thermal degradation by acting as radical traps.

Some other polyvinylchloride stabilizers have also been assumed to scavenge free radicals, since it has been shown that they retard the cobalt-catalyzed decomposition of t. butylhydroperoxide[45]. It is difficult to believe, however, that heavy metal salts could act in this way.

Frye and Horst have shown that when cadmium, barium or zinc carboxylates are heated with polyvinylchloride, some ester groups become attached to the polymer. They deduce that these replace labile chlorine atoms in the polymer which would otherwise initiate degradation[46,47]. They have similarly shown, using radioactive tracers, that with organotin stabilizers of formula Bu_2SnY_2 some of the Y groups become incorporated in the polymer[48]. Kenyon's observation[49] that butyl groups become attached to the polymer was not confirmed.

Other modes of action for stabilizers which have been proposed are that some are dienophiles, which break up long conjugated sequences, or that they catalyze the oxidation of polyene units, thus accelerating the known process of oxygen bleaching. None of these processes suggest there might be a common mode of action of all polyvinylchloride stabilizers. A general pattern of behaviour may be suggested, however, based on the following observations.

(*a*) Several investigators have shown that the rate of loss of HCl (free and combined) from degrading polyvinylchloride is not substantially altered by the presence of a variety of metal stabilizers[50,51,52], although the colour of the resin is improved.

(*b*) The number of double bonds formed during degradation is similarly unaltered in the presence or absence of cadmium or tin stabilizers[53].

Since the stabilizers reduce the conjugated chain length without altering the rate of formation of double bonds, they can formally be described as chain transfer agents. The most effective stabilizers, therefore, are those which keep the conjugated chain length well below that required for absorption in the visible to occur, and whose products of reaction with HCl are the least active as degradation promoters.

A recent explanation[52] of the synergistic effects frequently obtained with mixed polyvinylchloride stabilizers fits well into this picture. Cadmium stearate was found to be a better colour stabilizer than the barium salt, but cadmium chloride accelerates the decomposition of polyvinylchloride more readily than does the barium salt. In mixtures of the two, barium stearate preferentially absorbs the HCl, thus both preserving the more active colour stabilizer and reducing the rate of formation of the more active degradation catalyst.

Although this chapter has been confined to the chemistry of stabilizer action, it should be noted that, in practice, physical factors, such as the low solubility of oxygen in highly crystalline polymers, are particularly relevant to degradation processes and that stabilizer activity can be limited by volatility or poor compatibility. The most effective stabilizers, therefore, are those which most nearly meet both the chemical and physical requirements of a given plastics material.

REFERENCES

1. C. T. Handy and H. S. Rothrock, *J. Amer. Chem. Soc.*, 1958, **80**, 5306.
2. J. L. Bolland and H. Hughes, *J. Chem. Soc.*, 1949, 492.
3. G. H. Twigg, *Chem. and Ind.*, 1962, 4.
4. J. H. Chaudet and J. W. Tamblyn, *S.P.E. Trans.*, 1961, **1**, 57.
5. G. C. Newland and J. W. Tamblyn, *Amer. Chem. Soc., Divn., Polymer Chem.*, 1963, **4** (1), 230.
6. G. S. Hammond and N. J. Turro, *Amer. Chem. Soc. Divn. Polymer Chem.*, 1963, **4** (1), 224.
7. H. C. Bailey, *Ind. Chemist*, 1962, **38**, 215.
8. L. Bateman and K. R. Hargrave, *Proc. Roy. Soc.*, 1954, **A224**, 389.
9. C. Walling and R. Rabinowitz, *J. Amer. Chem. Soc.*, 1959, **81**, 1243.
10. B. D. Denning, W. F. Goodyear and B. Goldstein, *J. Amer. Chem. Soc.*, 1960, **82**, 1393.
11. E. A. Oberright, S. J. Leonardi and A. P. Kozacik, *Amer. Chem. Soc. Symposium*, "Additives in Lubricants", 1956, 115.
12. G. W. Kennerly and W. L. Patterson, *Ind. Eng. Chem.*, 1956, **48**, 1917.
13. L. Bateman, M. Cain, T. Colclough and J. I. Cunneen, *J. Chem. Soc.*, 1962, 3570.
14. R. B. Thompson, J. A. Chenicek and T. Symon, *Ind. Eng. Chem.*, 1952, **44**, 1659.
15. W. L. Hawkins and H. Sautter, *Chem. and Ind.*, 1962, 1825.
16. A. J. Chalk and J. F. Smith, *Trans. Faraday Soc.*, 1957, **53**, 1235.
17. A. J. Chalk and J. F. Smith, *Nature*, 1954, **174**, 802.
18. J. A. Howard and K. U. Ingold, *Can. J. Chem.*, 1962, **40**, 1851.
19. A. L. Buchachenko, K. Y. Kaganskaya and M. B. Neiman, *Kinetika i Kataliz*, 1961, **2**, 161.
20. J. R. Shelton and D. N. Vincent, *J. Amer. Chem. Soc.*, 1963, **85**, 2433.
21. A. L. Buchachenko, M. S. Khloplyankina and M. B. Neiman, *Doklady Akad. Nauk S.S.S.R.*, 1962, **143**, 146.
22. J. R. Thomas, *J. Amer. Chem. Soc.*, 1960, **82**, 5955.
23. K. U. Ingold, *Chem. Rev.*, 1961, **61**, 563.

24. G. Scott, *Chem. and Ind.*, 1963, 271.
25. J. A. Howard and K. U. Ingold, *Can. J. Chem.*, 1963, **41**, 1744.
26. A. F. Bickel and E. C. Kooyman, *J. Chem. Soc.*, 1956, 2215.
27. J. L. Bolland and P. ten Have, *Disc. Faraday Soc.*, 1947, No. 2, 252.
28. C. E. Boozer, G. S. Hammond, C. E. Hamilton and J. N. Sen, *J. Amer. Chem. Soc.*, 1955, **77**, 3233.
29. A. F. Bickel and E. C. Kooyman, *J. Chem. Soc.*, 1953, 3211.
30. R. B. Spacht, C. W. Wadelin, W. S. Hollingshead and D. C. Wills, *Ind. Eng. Chem. (Prod. Res. and Devel).*, 1962, **1**, 202.
31. B. M. Grieveson, R. N. Haward and B. Wright, *Soc. Chem. Ind.*, Monograph No. 13, 1961, 413.
32. L. G. Angert and A. S. Kuzminskii, *J. Polymer Sci.*, 1961, **55**, 489.
33. G. G. Knapp and H. D. Orloff, *Ind. Eng. Chem.*, 1961, **53**, 63.
34. N. P. Neureiter and D. E. Bown, *Ind. Eng. Chem. (Prod. Res. and Devel)*, 1962, **1**, 236.
35. W. L. Hawkins and F. H. Winslow, *Plastics Inst. Trans. and J.*, 1961, **29**, 82.
36. A. D. Delman, B. B. Simms and A. E. Ruff, *J. Polymer Sci.*, 1960, **45**, 415.
37. M. Braden and A. N. Gent, *J. Appl. Polymer Sci.*, 1960, **3**, 90.
38. M. Braden and A. N. Gent, *J. Appl. Polymer Sci.*, 1962, **6**, 449.
39. J. H. Thelin and A. R. Davis, *Rubber Age*, 1959, **86**, 81.
40. E. H. Andrews and M. Braden, *J. Appl. Polymer Sci.*, 1963, **7**, 1003.
41. W. S. Penn, "PVC Technology", Maclaren and Sons, London, 1962, 137.
42. Z. Kuri, H. Ueda and S. Shida, *J. Chem. Phys.*, 1960, **32**, 371.
43. Distillers Co. Ltd., French P. 1,275,340.
44. Distillers Co. Ltd., B.P. 932,992.
45. D. E. Winkler, *J. Polymer Sci.*, 1959, **35**, 3.
46. A. H. Frye and R. W. Horst, *J. Polymer Sci.*, 1959, **40**, 419.
47. A. H. Frye and R. W. Horst, *J. Polymer Sci.*, 1960, **45**, 1.
48. A. H. Frye, R. W. Horst and M. A. Paliobagis, *Amer. Chem. Soc., Divn. Polymer Chem.*, 1963 **4**, (1), 260.
49. A. S. Kenyon, *Nat. Bur. Stand. Circ.*, No. 525, 1953, 81.
50. E. J. Arlman, *J. Polymer Sci.*, 1954, **12**, 543.
51. L. H. Wartman, *Ind. Eng. Chem.*, 1955, **47**, 1013.
52. R. Nagatomi and Y. Saeki, *J. Polymer Sci.*, 1962, **61**, 560.
53. M. Imoto, *Chem. Abs.*, 1961, **55**, 24098.

CHAPTER 4

Correlation of Accelerated and Natural Weathering Tests

by C. A. BRIGHTON

WHEREAS MATERIALS such as steel, glass and wood, have been used for such long periods under widely different conditions that it is possible safely to predict their performance in almost any application, plastics have been in active service for only about twenty years. During this period, a limited amount of data has been obtained on the natural aging of plastics, but with the great technological improvements which have been effected during this time, much of this information has little bearing on the plastics available today. Plastics, however, have become firmly established as one of our basic raw materials and because of their obvious advantages— particularly reduced production costs – there is keen interest in their use for applications, such as in the building industry, where a long service life is essential. The knowledge that a particular plastic will give a performance at least as good as those of conventional materials has become, therefore, a prime requirement and this has led to the development of accelerated aging procedures where the materials are subjected to artificial weathering designed to simulate prolonged periods under natural conditions. Before comparing standard techniques in detail, however, it is advisable first to consider the changes which can take place in plastics compositions. As, however, the fundamental chemistry of weathering and degradation is discussed in detail in other chapters, it is necessary here to consider briefly only the ultimate properties which control the performance in any application.

All plastics can be made in a wide range of colours and it is essential that dyes and pigments should be used which do not change in colour on weathering. This is usually the first change which becomes apparent and it is of utmost importance when plastics materials are used for such purposes as protective coatings.

The stability of pigments has been studied exhaustively for many years but their performance when used for colouring plastics can be very different from that of the pigment by itself or in other media. Some plastics, such as polyvinylchloride, degrade when subjected to u.v. radiation and as this produces extensive colour changes, the ultimate change in colour may be due more to the instability of the plastic than to changes in the colour of the pigment employed.

This instability becomes apparent when changes in physical properties are followed. The fall-off in the impact strength of rubber-modified plastics, of which high-impact polystyrene is a typical example, can be of utmost importance when the material is used in applications where it may be subjected to sudden shocks. These changes are caused in the main by the ultra-violet portion of the solar spectrum representing about 4 per cent of the total intensity with wavelengths of 300–400 mμ. This does not mean, however, that other effects can be ignored, and heat, humidity and ozone can have significant effects.

Accelerated Aging Equipment

The equipment which is available for accelerated tests is designed to simulate normal weathering conditions at such an intensity as to give results in a much shorter time than would be encountered in practice. It is claimed for example that one hour in the Fade-O-Meter* corresponds to an outdoor exposure on the 50th parallel of one average day. Such a correlation can only be approximate because of the different weather conditions which exist during different seasons and also because of the various atmospheric conditions which prevail. In a heavy industrial area, there will be a considerable reduction in the u.v. content of the spectrum but the effects of this may be more than offset by those of industrial pollution.

The aging equipment used in the laboratory normally utilizes radiation produced by either the carbon arc or the xenon lamp with control of temperature and humidity. The samples are mounted in close proximity to the source of radiation so that the high intensity produces a condition of accelerated weathering. When a sample undergoes natural aging, it is subjected to constantly changing conditions which vary from darkness to bright sunlight and which differ according to the time of year. Because spectral energy distribution is so variable, daylight cannot be used

*Manufactured by *Atlas Electric Devices Ltd.*, Chicago, Ill., U.S.A.*

as a standard for assessing the suitability of artificial light sources. It is better to use the so-called global radiation for this purpose because, unlike sunlight, it always remains the same in the same geographical location. By global radiation is meant the radiation between 315 and 800 mµ falling on a horizontal plane from the sun and the sky on flat country on a cloudless day. To obtain effective

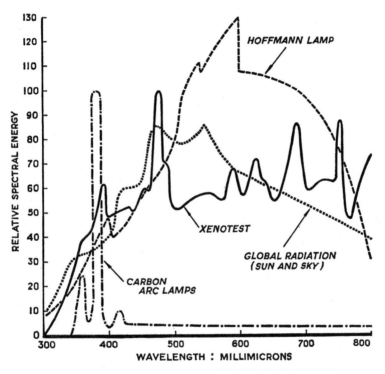

FIG. 17. SPECTRAL ENERGY DISTRIBUTION IN VARIOUS
TYPES OF ILLUMINATION

correlation between results obtained with laboratory aging equipment and those from natural aging experiments, it would appear essential to use a source of energy with a spectrum most closely resembling that of global radiation. Fig. 17 shows clearly that the spectral distribution of energy emitted by the xenon lamp when used with an ultra-violet filter is very similar to that of global radiation, whereas the curve for a carbon arc differs considerably.

The diagram also shows the spectrum of energy emitted by the Hoffman lamp which uses a tungsten filament lamp together with a mercury vapour lamp. Little has been published, however, with regard to aging studies with this lamp, as it has only recently become available.

The radiation emitted by an unfiltered xenon lamp has a short-wave ultra-violet component which is not found in normal daylight. It is essential that this is removed using an ultra-violet filter which does not allow transmission of wavelengths shorter than 295 mμ. The proportion of infra-red radiation from a xenon lamp is of greater intensity than in normal daylight, but this radiation generally has little destructive effect and the heat can be controlled by suitable means in the equipment. The radiation from a carbon arc lamp is very strong in the ultra-violet but weaker in the visible part of the spectrum compared with global radiation. This suggests that it should be easier to get some correlation between accelerated aging techniques and natural aging when using the xenon lamp rather than the carbon arc.

The Xenotest* uses a 1,500-watt high-pressure xenon arc lamp. A water filter removes a proportion of the infra-red radiation and, in addition, a high-speed fan cools the specimens to between 30 and 35 °C. The specimens (10 cm x 4·5 cm.) are held in frames which rotate around the arc at a distance of 3 in. from its centre and at a speed of 5 r.p.m. With each revolution of the frame, each sample carrier is rotated through 180° so that both sides of the holder can be used to hold specimens and this also permits of the effects of light and shade being simulated. Humidity is controlled in the cabinet by means of water sprays and can be adjusted up to 90–95 per cent relative humidity. It has been estimated that the intensity of the radiation at the surface of the samples is approximately the same as the maximum global radiation received on a horizontal surface in temperate latitudes in high summer.

The Weather-O-Meter† uses as its source of radiation a carbon arc which is enclosed in a glass globe. Attempts are made to reproduce the extremes encountered in natural aging by providing water sprays so that the samples can be subjected to complete wetting, either in the presence or in the absence of the radiation. The illumination and water spray can be controlled on a cyclic basis with a wide variety of conditions. Automatic humidity control can also be provided at any value between 20 and 60 per cent

---

* Manufactured by *Quarzlampen*, G.m.b.H., Hanau, Germany
† Manufactured by *Atlas Electrical Devices Ltd.*, Chicago, Ill., U.S.A.

over the full range of black panel temperatures between 60° and 95 °C.

The equipment produced by the same manufacturer and intended primarily for determining light-fastness is similar except that it is provided only with temperature and humidity control. A conversion kit is now available so that the carbon arc source can be changed for a xenon lamp (2,500 watts). Tentative relationships have been put forward by many workers for correlation of natural aging with accelerated aging on equipment using both the carbon arc and the xenon. These vary over a wide range, partly because of the different conditions under which the lamps have been operated and also because of the different aging aspects of the large number of materials which have been studied.

To obtain significant changes in a reasonable time, the laboratory equipment is fitted with lamps of high intensity and the samples are mounted close to the source so that they are subjected to the maximum radiation. Naturally, under such conditions a considerable amount of heat is generated and it is impossible to prevent an increase in the temperature of the samples. This can be reduced in most equipment by the provision of cooling fans; even so, the actual temperature of the samples may be anything from 30° to 70 °C. This means that in accelerated tests, the plastics material is subjected not only to the degradative effect of u.v. and the visible spectrum but also to a much higher temperature than would normally be encountered. Obviously a constant temperature is needed, if reproducible results or any reasonable degree of correlation are to be obtained.

In a recent study of the degradation of plasticized polyvinylchloride film[1], comparable effects were claimed to be obtainable with the Weather-O-Meter and the Fade-O-Meter so long as care is taken to maintain a black panel temperature at, or below, 140 °F. (60 °C). It has been shown also that good correlation with outdoor exposure is achieved at a temperature of 55 °C. This work was concerned with the different effects which arise when polyvinylchloride film degrades, and correlation was limited to the actual type of failure rather than to the time required to achieve it. Other work on unplasticized polyvinylchloride has confirmed that more reliable results are obtained at lower operating temperatures[2]. A sample of rigid polyvinylchloride containing 0·2 per cent of a u.v. absorber was found to undergo colour degradation after 950 hours when exposed on the Fade-O-Meter at 65 °C. If the temperature were reduced to 55 °C, the time required for failure increased to 1,350 hours. When the amount of u.v. absorber was raised to 0·4 per cent, the time to failure increased from 1,350 to 1,800 hours at 65 °C. Outdoor aging trials indicated that the 33 per cent improvement obtained at 55 °C, rather than the 16 per cent obtained at 65 °, was closer to results obtained during normal outdoor exposure.

The effect of humidity on the aging characteristics of most basic structural materials is well known and this factor is also of significance where the aging of plastics is concerned. Materials suffer far less in dry atmospheres than in regions of high humidity. This has become evident where natural weathering trials have been carried out in arid areas such as Arizona. Samples exposed in such areas are subjected to almost continuous sunshine for the greater part of the year but the changes are frequently less than would be experienced in humid conditions with less intense solar radiation.

The effects of humidity obviously vary with different materials but they are probably of most significance in cases where the plastics have a high moisture absorption. These comments indicate that it is essential to maintain strict control on the humidity conditions in any laboratory equipment, besides ensuring constant temperature control, if reproducible results are to be obtained. This is a primary consideration in any work designed to correlate accelerated aging tests with natural weathering. No one would suggest that, in any location, weather conditions over the year are the same from year to year, but even in the United Kingdom, where the summers are generally considered as "not what they used to be", there is surprisingly little variation. The differences in natural aging which may occur during different years are very small compared with the variations which can arise using accelerated tests. In spite of these difficulties, however, laboratory equipment can produce very useful data on the behaviour of plastics under natural conditions and correlation has been achieved in many instances.

Weathering of Dyes and Pigments

A change in appearance, and particularly in colour, is frequently the first indication that a plastic is undergoing degradation in service. The stability of dyes and pigments to natural radiation has long been determined by the blue wool scale[3] and this technique has also been used as a measurement of the colour fastness of plastics compositions. In this Standard, no detailed attention is given to the effect of variations in temperature, humidity or the type of atmosphere and it is probable that the dyestuffs used for colouring the wool standards are affected differently by these variables than would be, say, pigmented polyvinylchloride compounds.

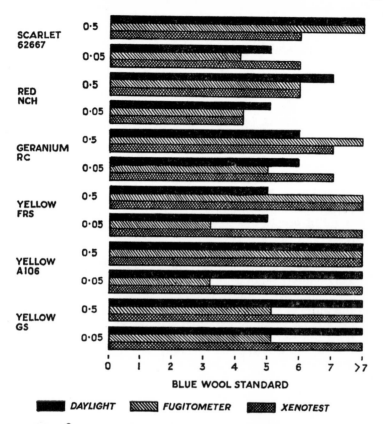

SCARLET
62667

RED
NCH

GERANIUM
RC

YELLOW
FRS

YELLOW
A106

YELLOW
GS

BLUE WOOL STANDARD

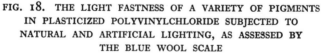

FIG. 18. THE LIGHT FASTNESS OF A VARIETY OF PIGMENTS
IN PLASTICIZED POLYVINYLCHLORIDE SUBJECTED TO
NATURAL AND ARTIFICIAL LIGHTING, AS ASSESSED BY
THE BLUE WOOL SCALE

This technique has the advantage that the natural light conditions under which the test is carried out do not affect the results by any significant amount and therefore the method should be readily suitable for accelerated aging. The author has examined a range of pigments in plasticized polyvinylchloride and assessed their light fastness on the blue wool scale using both natural and artificial light with the results shown in Fig. 18.

The Fugitometer used in these experiments has a carbon arc enclosed in a glass globe. No water filter is used and no attempt is made to control the relative humidity which is, therefore, very low.

The specimens held in frames rotate around, and are continuously exposed to, the arc at a distance of 9 in., the equipment being, in general, very similar to the Fade-O-Meter. The results clearly indicate that the same measure of light fastness is obtained irrespective of the light source which is used, but there are one or two differences which are worthy of note. The fading test was carried out at two pigment concentrations, *viz.*, 0·05 per cent and 0·5 per cent. At the higher concentration, there seems to be remarkably good correlation and it is quite evident that accelerated techniques can give useful indication of the light fastness of pigment in plastics compositions. With the lower amounts of pigment, such as are used for tinting, there is still good correlation between the Xenotest and daylight aging, but the Fugitometer seems to produce rather more rapid fading than would be encountered in practice. This might be due to the high u.v. content of the spectrum of the carbon arc.

The time needed to obtain the results in the laboratory, using the artificial light sources, is, of course, much less than that required to obtain them outside under natural conditions, because of the higher intensity of radiation. This is shown by Fig. 19 which gives the times of exposure under the three types of radiation and demonstrates, as would be expected, that the periods under natural conditions are the longer. Incidentally, the daylight time is recorded as the number of sunshine hours measured by the Campbell Stokes meter. Fig. 19 also shows that, with some pigments, the time required for fading is longer in the Fugitometer than in the Xenotest, but the converse is the more normal and to be expected because of the higher u.v. radiation from the carbon arc.

The results obtained do not permit of any correlation in time between the accelerated methods and outdoor exposure. This is due probably to the variation in humidity which must occur during natural weathering and also to the varying temperatures to which the pigmented specimens will rise when exposed to the sun. The recording of the natural exposure time as hours of sunshine is an attempt to differentiate between winter and summer conditions but even this is not entirely satisfactory because of the difference in the intensity of the sun during the various seasons.

The results, however, do lead to the following conclusions:

(*i*) The assessment of a pigment for light fastness on the blue wool scale can be carried out effectively using artificial sources.

(*ii*) The greater the exposure period required for fading as determined by accelerated weathering, the longer it will stand up to natural weathering.

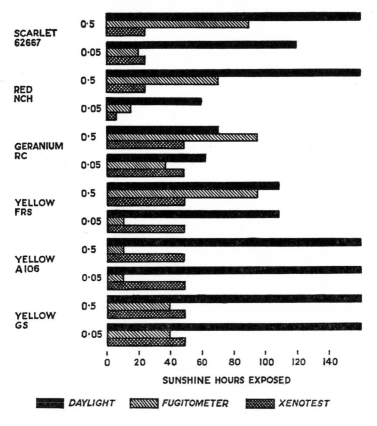

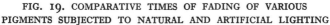

FIG. 19. COMPARATIVE TIMES OF FADING OF VARIOUS
PIGMENTS SUBJECTED TO NATURAL AND ARTIFICIAL LIGHTING

Degradation of Mechanical Properties

When the changes in physical properties which occur during outdoor exposure are considered, the problem of correlation with accelerated weathering becomes even more complex. Not only is it necessary to take into account humidity, temperature and radiation intensity and wavelength, but the size and shape of the sample and the conditions under which it was prepared, must also be considered. For example, the rate of fall-off of impact strength of toughened polystyrene will vary greatly with the thickness of the sample. All the standard tests used for the determination of physical properties require a number of specimens because they show a statistical distribution of values about the mean. Thus a detailed study of the fall-off of any particular property requires a large number of samples because each determination requires several specimens. This, in itself, is a problem because the accelerated weathering equipment is limited in size. Moreover, the production of a large number of specimens with uniform physical characteristics is extremely difficult. For example, if the samples are being moulded, it is essential to maintain constant press

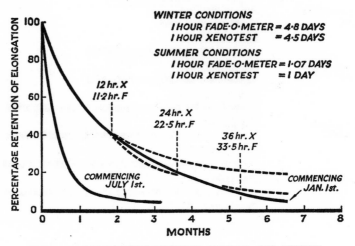

FIG. 20. COMPARISON BETWEEN SUMMER AND WINTER CONDITIONS ON THE AGING OF POLYSTYRENE AND THE RELATIONSHIP OF ACCELERATED TO NATURAL AGING

temperatures and to operate to a fixed moulding cycle. A technique whereby degradation can be followed without destruction of the sample therefore becomes of great value.

A number of publications concern work carried out in attempts to correlate the natural fall-off in physical properties with the results obtained in the laboratory[4-8]. It would appear that useful relationships do exist. The relationship, however, is specific, for each group of plastics, and results obtained with one material cannot necessarily be used to predict the natural life of another.

Results obtained on the degradation of polystyrene are shown in Fig. 20. The material was subjected to accelerated aging in the Fade-O-Meter and Xenotest and also to natural aging at different times of the year. The scale for the accelerated tests has been arranged so that the curve for natural aging (starting on January 1st) coincides with the curves obtained in the laboratory at 40 per cent retention of elongation at break. At this value, one hour in the Fade-O-Meter is equivalent to 4·8 days, and one hour in the Xenotest is equivalent to 4·5 days natural aging. The elongation at break under natural aging continues to fall-off steadily with time and eventually reaches zero. On the other hand, with accelerated tests there appears to be a minimum value which varies between 10 and 20 per cent, according to the light source. This has been

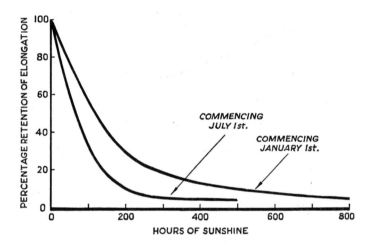

FIG. 21. COMPARATIVE EFFECT OF SUMMER AND WINTER
SUNSHINE ON THE DEGRADATION OF POLYSTYRENE

confirmed by continuing testing for as long as 9,000 hours. This difference between the ultimate values of elongation is of considerable interest and would justify further study. In practice, however, the useful life of a material is generally restricted to the period in which certain physical properties are reduced to 50 per cent of their initial values.

The difference in the rate of aging when this is carried out in the summer months, instead of in the period starting on the first of January is also shown in Fig. 20. Under summer conditions, one hour in the Fade-O-Meter is equivalent to 1·07 days and one hour in the Xenotest is equivalent to one day. This is in reasonable agreement with the manufacturers' claims. When the natural aging period runs into several years, the different effects of summer and winter conditions average out, but for short term assessments it is essential to take account of the season and to make a record of the weather conditions during the period of test.

If, instead of aging outdoors for a specific period, account is taken of the hours of sunshine which illuminate the sample, the effect of aging during different seasons is not so pronounced. In Fig. 21, the retention of elongation is plotted against hours of sunshine for the two periods instead of against total time of exposure. During the significant period of aging, *i.e.*, the time taken for the

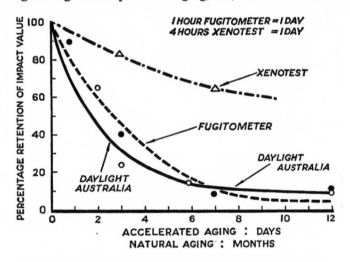

FIG. 22. EFFECT OF AGING IN AUSTRALIA ON THE IMPACT STRENGTH OF RUBBER-MODIFIED POLYVINYLCHLORIDE AND THE RELATIVE EFFECTS OF ACCELERATED AGING TESTS

elongation at break to drop to 50 per cent of its original value, there is only a small difference between aging during winter sunshine and summer sunshine. The difference in aging effect is, therefore, not so apparent when tests are carried out in tropical climates, due to the hours of sunshine experienced during the winter. For example, in Sydney, Australia, during 1959, the hours of sunshine for the month varied only from 157 in June to 232 in November.

A comparison of the effects of aging a rubber-modified polyvinylchloride in the Fugitometer and Xenotest with the results of natural aging in Australia is given in Fig. 22. The Fugitometer is similar to the Fade-O-Meter and produces the same effect in one hour as that obtained with natural aging in one day. Results with the Xenotest, however, show a marked difference, probably due to the different temperatures which the samples attain. In the Xenotest, the water filter and cooling fan give an ambient temperature of 30–35 °C, whereas the Fugitometer is not fitted with cooling devices and the temperature of the specimen is about 55 °C. In this case, the final value to which the impact strength falls when using the Fugitometer is almost identical with that obtained in natural aging.

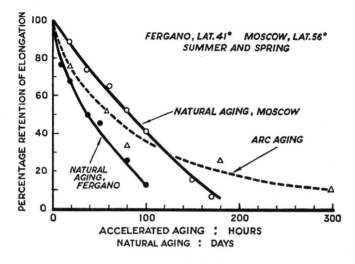

FIG. 23. EFFECT OF NATURAL WEATHERING AT TWO LATITUDES IN RUSSIA ON THE DEGRADATION OF POLYETHYLENE AND THE RELATIVE EFFECT OF ACCELERATED AGING TESTS

Attention has already been drawn to the fact that the size of specimen can have an influence on the rate at which some materials degrade. The rubber-modified polyvinylchloride used in this work was aged in the form of a sheet 6 in. square and ⅛ in. thickness. On return, the specimens were cut to shape and notched for determination of impact strength by the Izod method. These particular dimensions were chosen because it was felt that they were typical of those likely to be encountered in practice. When the same material was aged in the form of moulded bars of ½ in. thickness, there was only a 50 per cent reduction of impact strength, even after aging for five years in Florida.

A recent publication[9] gives results obtained following a study of the changes in physical and mechanical properties of polyethylene and plasticized polyvinylchloride during atmospheric and artificial aging. The authors concluded that a useful correlation could be obtained from equipment using a twin carbon arc as the source of illumination, but that results as meaningful were produced from equipment using mercury lamps. Fig. 23 shows the rate of change in the elongation at break of polyethylene when aged under the carbon arc source and under natural conditions at Moscow (latitude 56°) and at Fergano, in the south of Russia on a latitude of 41°. If the results are considered only as far as 50 per cent retention of elongation, the three curves can be considered as straight lines and a useful correlation is obtained. It is interesting to note that the results suggest that, under artificial aging, the elongation reaches a minimum value, whereas under natural aging the elongation falls off to zero. This is in agreement with the results given above for polystyrene.

Non-Destructive Testing

The work which has been reported up to now has made very little contribution to an understanding of those factors which are responsible for the changes that occur in plastics on weathering. It is quite impossible with the equipment now available to separate the effects of temperature, radiation, humidity and moisture. If the role which these factors play can be studied individually, then it should be possible to design accelerated aging equipment which would be capable of a more accurate simulation of the aging of plastics under natural conditions.

A further limitation to a better understanding is the nature of the test procedures which are used for the assessment of the changes in physical properties. These tests involve destruction of the samples and thus an extensive programme requires many hundreds of specimens. The difficulty of preparing such a number with uniform physical properties has already been mentioned.

Test methods which do not involve destruction of the sample could enable a more comprehensive study to be made and some progress has already been reported. This is limited at present to polystyrene but undoubtedly in due course other plastics will be examined by non-destructive techniques. Since dynamic mechanical results can be related to molecular structure, molecular weight and composition, it should be possible to obtain a relationship between dynamic behaviour and the mechanisms controlling fracture of polymers under impact.

Karas and Warburton[10] have suggested on theoretical grounds that the loss tangent at any temperature may be presumed to be related to the first order derivative of the modulus at that temperature. They propose that the toughness of this material be measured by the ratio of the modulus in the glassy state to the modulus in the rubbery state. This can be expressed as the log of the ratio

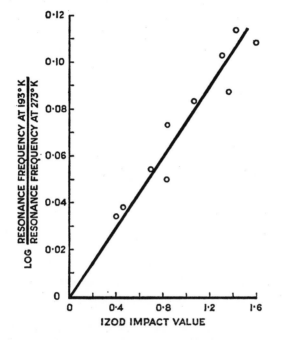

FIG. 24. RELATIONSHIP BETWEEN DYNAMIC MECHANICAL FREQUENCY RATIO AND THE IMPACT STRENGTH OF RUBBER-MODIFIED POLYSTYRENE

of the resonance frequencies between two temperatures, at one of which the material is in the glassy state and at one in the rubbery state. The results which have been obtained for a range of rubber-modified polystyrenes are shown in Fig. 24 where the log of the ratio of resonance frequency at 193 °K to that at 273 °K is plotted against the Izod impact strength.

Comments from other workers in this field suggest that this relationship is purely fortuitous, since it was obtained by varying the rubber content of the polystyrene. This would have the result of altering both impact strength and dynamic elastic parameters simultaneously without necessarily introducing a syllogistic relationship. No experimental work has yet been carried out on following the change in impact strength during the aging process. The failure of materials due to weathering may be attributable to surface changes and, if this is so, it is possible that a change in impact strength due to degradation would have far less effect on the dynamic properties that would be obtained by varying the rubber content. There is no doubt, however, that studies of this type will

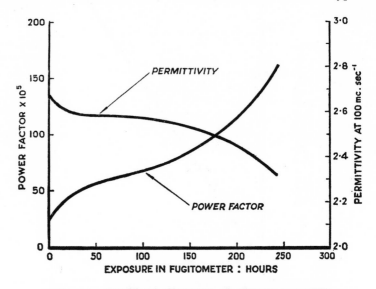

FIG. 25. EFFECT OF EXPOSURE OF RUBBER-MODIFIED
POLYSTYRENE ON POWER FACTOR AND ELECTRICAL PERMITTIVITY

lead to a better understanding of the physical properties of plastics materials and this will help in following the changes which occur during weathering.

When polystyrene undergoes degradation under the influence of u.v. radiation, there are changes in the electrical properties of the material. In the laboratories of British Geon Ltd., changes in electrical power factor and permittivity which occur on aging have been studied, and it has been found that the decrease in permittivity of polystyrene with exposure in the Fugitometer is much smaller than is the corresponding increase in power factor. Thus determination of the latter would appear to be the more promising method of test. The rate of increase in power factor of a sample of blue polystyrene, when exposed in the Fugitometer, is about 1·5 per cent per hour and results suggest that the rate is fairly steady up to a time of 350 hours exposure (Fig. 25). So far, this work has not gone beyond the preliminary stages and it has not yet been possible to establish the relationship between power factor and such physical properties as impact strength and elongation at break.

Conclusions

It will be apparent from the foregoing that no reliable techniques have been established which will permit precise prediction of the natural life of a plastics material. The published work, however, has given an indication of some of the pitfalls to be avoided and unless these are understood, misleading results may be obtained. Some laboratory equipment which is in use at present has not been designed to give controlled weathering but rather uncontrolled degradation which has little relation to conditions encountered in natural aging. With such equipment any correlation between natural and artificial aging may be somewhat fortuitous. Obviously there is a need for more precise work in this field of the aging of plastics, particularly in relation to the long-term behaviour of plastics outdoors. For short term applications, accelerated aging tests can already be used with a high degree of confidence.

REFERENCES

1. A. L. Scarborough, S.P.E. Technical Papers, 15.11.61.
2. Hans-Helmut Frey, *Kunststoffe*, 1962, **52,** 667.
3. British Standard., 1006, 1955.
4. Hans-Helmut Frey, *Kunststoffe*, 1963, **53,** 103.
5. J. B. de Coste and V. T. Wallder, *Ind. Eng. Chem.*, 1955, **47,** 319.
6. A. G. Bussell, *Trans. Inst. Rubber Ind.*, 1961, **37,** 43.
7. M. J. Moreaux, *Ind. Plast. Modernes*, 1961, **13** (8), 25.
8. F. W. Reinhart, *S.P.E. News*, Sept., 1948, **4,** 3.
9. G. O. Tatevosyan and I. B. Kuznetsova, *Plasticheskie Massy*, 1962 (3), 44. English Translation: *Soviet Plastics*, 1962 (3), 38.
10. G. C. Karas and B. Warburton, *Plast. Inst. Trans and J.*, 1962, **30,** 198.
11. H. Burns. Private Communication.

CHAPTER 5

Thermal Degradation
of Polyvinylchloride

by W. I. BENGOUGH

POLYVINYLCHLORIDE is thermally unstable at temperatures above 150°C., decomposing to give hydrogen chloride and a polymeric product which is brown or black in colour depending upon the extent of degradation. The reactions involved in the thermal degradation are complex and involve chain scission and cross-linking, as well as dehydrochlorination of the polymer chains. Such reactions can be represented as follows:

Dehydrochlorination

$$\cdots\cdots CH_2-CHCl\cdots\cdots \longrightarrow \cdots\cdots CH=CH\cdots\cdots + HCl$$

Cross-linking

$$\cdots\cdots + \cdots\cdots \longrightarrow \begin{array}{c} \cdots\cdots \\ | \\ \cdots\cdots \end{array}$$

Chain scission

$$\cdots\cdots\cdots\cdots \longrightarrow \cdots\cdots + \cdots\cdots$$

In air

$$\cdots\cdots + O_2 \longrightarrow \begin{array}{c} OOH \\ | \\ \cdots\cdots \end{array}$$

At high temperatures

$$\cdots\cdots \xrightarrow{\;>300°C\;} \text{aromatic and aliphatic hydrocarbons}$$
(HCl evolved below 250°C.)

Of the above reactions, dehydrochlorination has been most fully studied, and it is with this reaction that this chapter is primarily concerned.

The Dehydrochlorination Reaction

Early studies on the thermal degradation of polyvinylchloride revealed that, at temperatures in the region of 200 °C., the polymer changes fairly quickly from colourless to a pale brown, darkens rapidly and finally becomes black. Simultaneously with the intensification of colour, hydrogen chloride is liberated from the polymer.

The elimination of hydrogen chloride from the polymer leads to unsaturation, but the colour formation can only arise if the unsaturated double bonds formed are conjugated. Accordingly, it seems likely that hydrogen chloride molecules peel off successively along the polymer chains leaving conjugated polyene chains which are responsible for selective light absorption and colour.

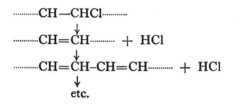

This progressive dehydrochlorination process is favoured in that, once one double bond has been formed in a polymer molecule, the bond strengths of the hydrogen and chlorine atoms attached to carbon atoms adjacent to the double bond are lowered by allylic activation. Thus one or other of these atoms is likely to make up the next molecule of hydrogen chloride to be eliminated from the polymer molecule.

It is now fairly well established that the above type of elimination of hydrogen chloride does occur. What is not generally agreed upon is the precise mechanism of the reaction. Early workers thought that the dehydrochlorination reaction was autocatalytic, *i.e.*, the hydrogen chloride evolved was a catalyst for the reaction. The probable reason for this view was that basic salts, such as basic lead carbonate, were known to be heat stabilizers for polyvinylchloride. In 1953, however, it was shown by Druesedow and Gibbs[1] that hydrogen chloride was not a cataylst for the degradation reaction and this was confirmed a year later by Arlman[2]. Accordingly, stabilization of polyvinylchloride by basic salts cannot be explained in this simple manner and the mechanism is still not fully understood.

Arlman made what seems to be a major step forward in the understanding of the mechanism of the thermal degradation of

polyvinylchloride by showing that small amounts of free radical initiators, such as benzoyl peroxide and azo-bis-isobutyronitrile,
when added to polyvinylchloride, produced an appreciable increase in the rate of evolution of hydrogen chloride[2]. He suggested
a free radical mechanism for the dehydrochlorination reaction,
which would also explain the finding of Druesedow and Gibbs[1]
that the presence of oxygen leads to an increase in the rate of
dehydrochlorination, in as much as oxidation is known to involve
free radical reactions. Arlman's suggested scheme[2] for the dehydrochlorination reaction is given below:

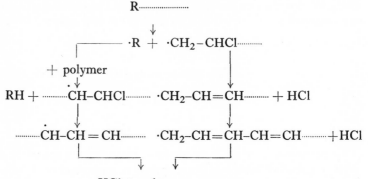

nHCl + polyene structure

The initiation process involves the scission of a chain end
group, or the abstraction of a hydrogen atom from a polymer
chain, to give a polymer radical followed by the elimination of
hydrogen chloride to give an allylic radical. Propagation then
occurs by consecutive elimination of hydrogen chloride along the
polymer chain giving rise to the formation of a polyene [3, 18]. From
a comparison with low molecular weight polyenes, it appears that
from seven to sixteen conjugated double bonds are necessary to
give rise to the initial coloration exhibited by the degraded polymer. The length of the sequence of conjugated double bonds in the
polyene chain is determined either by chain transfer reactions with
other polymer molecules or by interaction with a second free
radical. If termination occurs by combination of polymer free
radicals, the reaction would lead to cross-links being formed.

More recently, Winkler in a review paper[4] suggested that
chlorine atoms are the chain carriers in the dehydrochlorination reaction, and that the propagation proceeds by the following reaction.

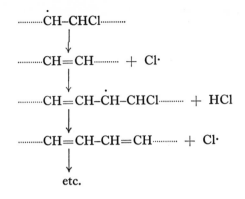

This mechanism suggests that as each free chlorine atom is formed, it abstracts a hydrogen atom from the adjacent $>CH_2$ group, forming a molecule of hydrogen chloride and a free radical which again reverts to a stable molecule by elimination of a chlorine atom. It is perhaps a little difficult to understand why the chlorine atom, if it is truly a "free" atom, does not diffuse rapidly from the site of its formation and attack another polymer molecule or another region of the same polymer chain. When degradation occurs in solution, free chlorine atoms would be expected readily to attack the solvent molecules. Yet there is no evidence of any reduction of the colouration for solution degradation compared with bulk polymer degradation. Termination of the sequence of conjugated double bonds, according to Winkler, occurs by abstraction of a hydrogen atom from a $>CHCl$ group in the polymer molecule or a hydrogen atom from another polymer molecule or by interaction between chloride atoms and/or polymer radicals.

From the work of Baum and Wartman[5], it seems probable that initiation of the dehydrochlorination process occurs at carbon atoms adjacent to carbon-carbon double bonds present in the polymer. These workers showed that mild chlorination of polyvinylchloride led to a considerably lower rate of degradation, and from this it was presumed that the chlorination process saturated a number of the double bonds in the polymer. They also showed, by chemical means, that double bonds exist in normal polyvinylchloride, and pointed out that terminal double bonds were likely to arise as the result of chain transfer reactions with the monomer during polymerization.

Such reactions are known to control the molecular weight of the polyvinylchloride[6]. Chlorine-bearing tertiary carbon atoms located at branch points along the polymer chain, were suggested as sources of secondary initiation[5]. These were expected to play a greater role at slightly higher temperatures (above 150°C) and at later stages of degradation. Finally, using 4-chloro-hexene-2 as a model, Baum and Wartman showed that the activation energy for the dehydrochlorination of this molecule was 22·5 kcal. mole[-1] which is within the range of values[2,7-12] reported for the dehydrochlorination of polyvinylchloride.

Studies by Stromberg, Straus and Achhammer[7] of changes in the infra-red spectrum of polyvinylchloride at various stages of degradation at temperatures in the range 100–400°C showed that carbon-chlorine bonds disappear and are replaced by carbon-carbon double bonds and aromatic structures. Using a mass spectrometric method for analysing the products, it was further demonstrated that at temperatures below 250°C, the main product of the thermal degradation is hydrogen chloride, whereas at higher temperatures secondary decomposition takes place, the products being mainly aliphatic and aromatic hydrocarbons[7].

The formation of aromatic hydrocarbons could be explained by the cyclization of the ends of polyene chains, while the aliphatic hydrocarbons would arise from chain scission reactions. These workers used three samples of polyvinylchloride obtained (a) using benzoyl peroxide as initiator, (b) using azo-bis-isobutyronitrile as initiator, and (c) by irradiation with γ rays. At temperatures above 220°C., the azo-initiated polymer decomposed more rapidly than did the other two samples. In all three cases, the rate of degradation decreased markedly after about 58 per cent loss in weight had occurred. Plotting loss in weight against time, they found that the rate was proportional to the 3/2 power of the polymer concentration, and they claimed that this supported a free radical mechanism for the degradation process, involving second order termination between chain carrier radicals. This is clearly an oversimplification, since it is known that the rate depends upon various structural features in the initial polymer. Obviously, the structures would be very different long before a 50 per cent loss in weight had occurred.

Studying the thermal degradation of polyvinylchloride as powder and as film at temperatures in the range 220–200°C, Talamini and Pezzin[11] found that the rate was inversely proportional to the molecular weight of the polymer, indicating that degradation is initiated at the chain ends. They showed that the rate is independent of the nitrogen flow rate, which confirms that hydrogen chloride does not catalyse the degradation, and they observed no difference in the initial rate of degradation in the presence or absence of oxygen. However, the rate increased with time when degradation was carried out in the presence of oxygen, while it remained constant under nitrogen. One other significant difference is that the activation energy was much lower in oxygen than in nitrogen, *viz.*, 24 kcal. mole[-1] for the former and 33 kcal. mole[-1] for the latter.

In nearly all the above-mentioned work, the polyvinylchloride has been degraded either as a film or as a powder. Any rate measurements will therefore involve both chemical reactions during dehydrochlorination and diffusion of hydrogen chloride out of the film or powdered mass of polymer. It is quite possible, at lower temperatures or with thick films, that the observed rate of dehydrochlorination could be entirely determined by the rate of diffusion of hydrogen chloride out of the polymer film and not by the chemical reactions leading to its formation. For this reason, it is desirable to study the degradation in solution. Further advantages of carrying out degradation in solution are that this permits the polymer concentration to be widely varied and the initial rate of dehydrochlorination to be determined, *i.e.*, when only a few per cent of the available chlorine has been liberated (as hydrogen chloride) from the polymer. On the other hand, in bulk degradation, one would require to pursue the degradation to a late stage to obtain the effect of a variation in polymer concentration. Even then, it is difficult to determine the concentration accurately, since in general the density of the degraded polymer is different from that of the original polymer. Frequently this effect is ignored. The chief disadvantage of studying solution degradation is that the solvent might affect the mechanism of the degradation process. However, such studies would more closely simulate the degradation behaviour of plasticized polyvinylchloride, in as much as plasticizers constitute high temperature solvents.

Work on the degradation of polyvinylchloride in solution has recently been carried out by Sharpe[12] and Varma[13] in the laboratories of the Royal College of Science and Technology, Glasgow. In most of this work, ethyl benzoate was used as solvent, but some results have been obtained with *o*-dichlorobenzene, dichloronaphthalene, benzophenone, dioctylphthalate, tritolylphosphate and nitrobenzene. Of these solvents, nitrobenzene is the only one which behaves in an exceptional way. Thus, while the initial rates with all the other solvents remain constant (although frequently different), the initial rate with nitrobenzene increases rapidly and this is accompanied by a rapid blackening of the polymer solution.

Clearly, nitrobenzene has an interfering effect on the degradation process, and experimental results using this solvent bear little or no relation to the bulk degradation of polyvinylchloride. The constant rate of loss of HCl when various concentrations of polyvinylchloride solutions in ethyl benzoate are heated is shown in Fig. 26.

The dependence of the rate of dehydrochlorination upon the polymer concentration was found[12] to be first order in ethyl benzoate solution at temperatures between 178° and 212°C. When

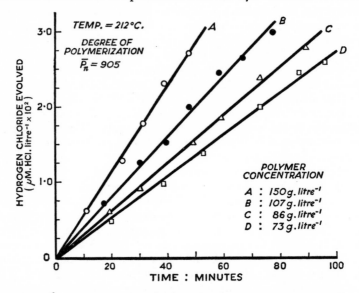

FIG. 26. EFFECT OF POLYMER CONCENTRATION ON THE RATE OF DEGRADATION OF POLYVINYLCHLORIDE IN ETHYL BENZOATE SOLUTION

polymers of different molecular weight were compared as shown in Fig. 27, it was found that the lower molecular weight material degraded faster for a given weight concentration of polymer. However, when rates for equimolar concentration of polymers of various molecular weights were compared, they were found to be approximately equal, and the rate of degradation could be represented by a single equation, e.g., at 212°C:

$$\text{rate} = 3 \cdot 62 \times 10^{-3} \, c_n \text{ moles HCl litre}^{-1} \text{ sec.}^{-1}$$

where c_n is the polymer concentration in polymoles per litre. This result strongly supports the view that initiation of dehydrochlorination takes place at the end of a polymer molecule, and since chain transfer with monomer controls the molecular weight of polyvinylchloride[6], it seems reasonable to suggest that a group with the following structure is responsible for initiation.

$$CHCl = CH–CHCl–CH_2–$$

The overall activation energy for the dehydrochlorination was not affected by the molecular weight of the polymer over the range studied and was found[12] to be about 23 kcal. mole[-1] which is sur-

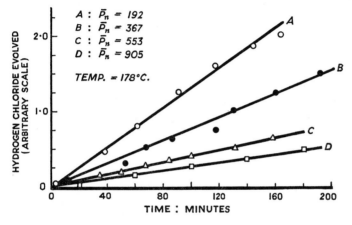

FIG. 27. EFFECT OF VARIATION IN THE DEGREE OF POLYMERIZATION ON THE RATE OF DEGRADATION FOR A FIXED WEIGHT CONCENTRATION OF POLYVINYLCHLORIDE IN ETHYL BENZOATE

prisingly close to the value of 22·5 kcal. mole[-1] reported by Baum and Wartman for 4-chloro-2-hexene[5]. This provides further evidence for allylic activation of the C-Cl bond.

If the hypothesis that dehydrochlorination proceeds by a free radical chain mechanism is accepted, it might be expected that the addition of free radical catalysts to polymer solutions, would lead to a measurable rate of degradation at temperatures of 20° or 30° below the normal temperature for a measurable rate of degradation. The addition of 2 per cent azo-bis-isobutyronitrile or benzoyl peroxide (wt./wt. polymer) to ethyl benzoate solutions of polyvinylchloride at temperatures up to 150°C, however, gave no measurable increase in rate. Some increase in rate was observed, however, when benzoyl peroxide was added to powdered polymer[13] and heated in the absence of solvent. At higher temperatures, *e.g.*, 212°C, the rate of degradation in ethyl benzoate solution was doubled by the addition of 4 per cent azo-bis-isobutyronitile and larger quantities increased the rate still further.

These results can be explained if, in solution, dimerization of the free radicals is fast compared with the rate of radical attack upon the polymer molecules, or if the radicals selectively attack the solvent molecules to give relatively stable radicals (*e.g.*, by addition to the benzene ring) which will not subsequently attack the polymer chains. If this latter suggestion is correct, however, it is difficult to understand why chlorine atoms do not likewise attack the solvent, in which case the solvent might be expected to retard the rate of degradation. There is no evidence of this. In fact, results have indicated that the rate of degradation in solution is of the same order of magnitude as in bulk, when allowance is made for concentration effects.

An alternative explanation of the catalytic effect of azo-bis-isobutyronitrile at 212°C is that the free radicals derived from the catalyst assist in the formation of double bonds in the polymer by the following type of reactions:

$$R\cdot + \text{------}CH_2\text{--}CHCl\text{------} \rightarrow RH + \text{------}\overset{\cdot}{C}H\text{--}CHCl\text{------}$$
$$R\cdot + \text{------}\underset{\cdot}{C}H\text{--}CHCl\text{------} \rightarrow RCl + \text{------}CH = CH\text{------}$$

The double bonds then become sites for initiating dehydrochlorination reactions.

The presence of oxygen had no effect on the rate of dehydrochlorination in solution but it did lead to an increase in the rate of degradation of powdered polyvinylchloride[11,12]. This difference in behaviour may arise because the concentration of oxygen dissolved in the polymer solution at 212°C is too low to have an appreciable effect upon the rate. Oxygen, however, did cause a rapid blackening of the solution, accompanied by chain scission reactions.

The addition of free radical inhibitors, such as 1,4–diaminoanthraquinone and tetrachloro-dibenzoquinone, either had no effect on the rate or slightly enhanced it. A dibutyl tin stabilizer (Stanclere 70) reduced the rate to approximately 15 per cent of the normal over various periods depending upon the quantity of stabilizer added. This result would seem to indicate that the dehydrochlorination proceeds by at least two mechanisms. It has been claimed that dibutyl tin stabilizers are free radical inhibitors[14] but relatively little fundamental work has been reported on such systems, and the mechanism of such reactions is still not fully understood.

Some support for the free radical mechanism of dehydrochlorination of polyvinylchloride has been obtained from ESR measurements[15] on samples of irradiated polymer. From work reported in the literature[15-18], it is clear that free radicals are formed when polyvinylchloride is subjected to γ irradiation at low temperatures, and that hydrogen chloride is evolved on warming up the polymer. Furthermore, the polymer develops a brown colouration. It may be concluded therefore that free radicals can initiate dehydrochlorination of polyvinylchloride. It does not prove, however, that in the thermal degradation the mechanism is necessarily a free radical one, and the precise mechanism of the reaction is still obscure.

The Cross-linking Reaction

Although it has been known for some time that polyvinylchloride becomes insoluble following thermal degradation at temperatures in the region of 200°C, until recently no attempt had been made to measure the rate of the cross-linking reaction or to study its mechanism. It has been suggested that cross-linking arises due to the random combination of polymer radicals which initially leads to larger molecules and eventually to a cross-linked network[4,8]. While the possibility of such radical-recombination reactions cannot be disputed, results from recent work suggest that this is not the main reaction leading to a cross-linked network structure[23].

One of the chief difficulties in studying the cross-linking process is that the usual solution techniques of examining molecular size cannot be applied once the polymer is cross-linked and an insoluble and infusible network has been formed. It is possible, however, to calculate the rate of cross-linking from the rate of accumulation of gel, for instance, during a trifunctional polycondensation reaction, and there seems no reason why this technique should not be applied equally well to the degradation of polymers. The theory of the process was developed mainly by Flory and Stockmayer[19-22] and is outlined below.

Flory has shown that for a system composed of polymer molecules all of equal chain length, an infinite network will be formed if there is at least one cross-linked unit for each primary chain originally present. Thus the gel point will occur when the number of cross-linked units is equal to the number of primary chains initially present. The relationship between the critical probability

(x_c) at the gel point that any unit of a primary chain has cross-linked, and the degree of polymerization (P) is given by the equation:

$$x_c = 1/(P-1) \simeq 1/P \quad \dots \quad \dots \quad \dots \quad \dots \quad (1)$$

Flory has also shown that, if the polymer molecules are of different chain lengths, this equation then becomes

$$x_c = 1/(\bar{P}_w - 1) \simeq 1/\bar{P}_w \quad \dots \quad \dots \quad \dots \quad (2)$$

where $\bar{P}_w$ is the weight-average degree of polymerization.

For a random distribution typical of vinyl polymers, the number-average degree of polymerization $\bar{P}_n$ is equal to $\bar{P}_w/2$.

$$\text{Thus } x_c \simeq 1/2\, \bar{P}_n \quad \dots \quad \dots \quad \dots \quad \dots \quad \dots \quad (3)$$

If therefore $\bar{P}_w$ and $\bar{P}_n$ are known and the time for gelation (t_g) to occur is determined, then the rate of cross-link formation can be calculated in the following way.

Let c be the concentration of the polymer solution in grams per litre. If M is the molecular weight of the monomer, then c/M is the concentration in monomoles per litre and $c/M\bar{P}_n$ in polymoles per litre. At the gel point there will be $c/M\bar{P}_w$ cross-linked units per litre of solution.

If a random molecular weight distribution (*i.e.*, $\bar{P}_w = 2\,\bar{P}_n$) be assumed, then the average rate of cross-link formation (R_c) up to the time of gelation will be given by

$$R_c = c/4\, M\, \bar{P}_n\, t_g \dots \quad \dots \quad \dots \quad \dots \quad \dots \quad \dots \quad (4)$$

Now, let the order of the cross-linking reaction be y with respect to the polymer concentration, *i.e.*,

$$R_c = k\,(c/M\, \bar{P}_n)^y \quad \dots \quad \dots \quad \dots \quad \dots \quad \dots \quad (5)$$

where k is the rate constant for the cross-linking reaction.

Equating equations (4) and (5),

$$k = 1/4\, t_g\,(c/M\, \bar{P}_n)^{y-1} \quad \dots \quad \dots \quad \dots \quad \dots \quad (6)$$

From equation (6) it is clear that, if the reaction is first order, the gel time will be constant, *i.e.*, independent of the polymer concentration, whereas if it is second order, the gel time will be inversely proportional to the concentration.

Fig. 28 shows that when polyvinylchloride solutions in ethyl benzoate were heated at temperatures in the range 178°–212 °C, t_g increased with decrease in polymer concentration[23]. With polymer of lower molecular weight ($\bar{P}_n$ up to 550), t_g was found to be nearly inversely proportional to the polymer concentration as shown in Fig. 29 and the order of the cross-linking reaction was found to be between 1·9 and 2·2 with respect to the polymer concentration. For higher molecular weight polymer ($\bar{P}_n = 905$), the order of the reaction was found to be 2·5.

These results indicate that the cross-linking reaction is approximately second order, but some explanation for the rather high figure of 2·5 is needed. This could arise if intramolecular cross-linking occurs to an appreciable extent with the higher molecular weight polymer. Intermolecular and intramolecular

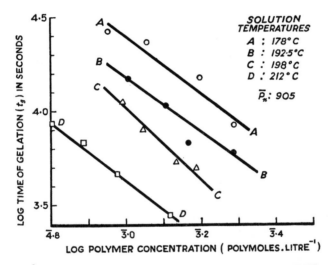

FIG. 28. VARIATION OF TIME OF GELATION WITH POLYMER CONCENTRATION FOR POLYVINYLCHLORIDE IN ETHYL BENZOATE SOLUTION AT VARIOUS TEMPERATURES

cross-linking are likely to occur in different proportions at different polymer concentrations, the latter being favoured at low polymer concentrations.

Since intramolecular cross-linking will not contribute to the formation of an infinite network, it will not affect the time for gelation, and therefore the total rate of cross-link formation (*i.e.*, intermolecular and intramolecular cross-linking) will be greater than that estimated from the time for gelation, particularly at low polymer concentrations. For low molecular weight polymer, intramolecular cross-linking is less likely, partly because of the shorter chains and also because higher concentrations of the polymers have to be used to avoid unduly prolonged gel times.

Table 2 shows that the time for gelation for a fixed weight concentration of polymer varies approximately inversely with the molecular weight of the polymer. This is to be expected, since even if the rate of cross-link formation were the same for polymers of different molecular weight, the time for gelation would be greater for the lower molecular weight polymer than for the higher polymer since a greater number of cross-links are required to produce an infinite network structure. The actual rate of cross-link formation calculated from times for gelation for a fixed weight concentration of polymer in ethyl benzoate solution was found to be fairly constant, varying relatively from 1·0 to 1·4 (in arbitrary units) for a four-fold variation in polymer molecular weight.

TABLE 2. EFFECT OF DEGREE OF POLYMERIZATION OF THE POLYMER ON THE RATE CONSTANT FOR CROSS-LINKING, THE TIME OF GELATION AND THE RELATIVE RATE OF CROSS-LINKING FOR A FIXED WEIGHT CONCENTRATION OF THE POLYMER SAMPLES AT 198°C.

$\bar{P}_n$		k $(l.polymole^{-1}$ $sec.^{-1}. 10^2)$		t_g $(sec. 10^3)$		Relative rate of cross-link formation (arbitrary units)
905	...	3·30	...	4·98	...	1·0
553	...	1·80	...	5·62	...	1·4
367	...	0·65	...	9·0	...	1·2
192	...	0·20	...	17·2	...	1·35

The lower value pertained to the polymer of highest molecular weight, and might be due to the occurrence of intramolecular cross-linking suggested previously. If the rate of cross-link formation per given weight concentration of polymer can be taken to be independent of the molecular weight of the polymer, then each structural unit in a polymer molecule has the same chance of undergoing cross-linking whether it is part of a large or small polymer molecule. This implies that allylic activation has little effect on the cross-linking process, which is in marked contrast to its effect on the dehydrochlorination reaction. A random condensation between structural units of polymer molecules with the elimination of HCl seems to be the simplest explanation of the mechanism of the thermal cross-linking of polyvinylchloride in solution.

The overall activation energy for the cross-linking reaction which did not vary with the molecular weight of the polymer was found to be approximately 23 kcal. mole⁻¹ over the temperature range (178°–212°C.) studied. This is remarkably close to that for the dehydrochlorination reaction. However, even if both reactions are free radical processes, as has been suggested by a number o workers[4,8], the activation energies would be expected to differ since the orders of the reactions with respect to the free radical concentration are different.

Enthalpy calculations show that the cross-linking reaction is exothermic to the extent of 2·8 kcal. mole^{-1}, whereas random dehydrochlorination would be endothermic to about 16·6 kcal. mole^{-1}. If, however, dehydrochlorination occurs *via* allylic activa-

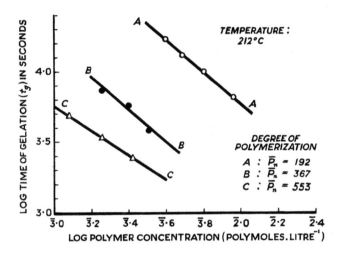

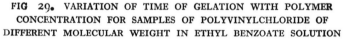

FIG 29. VARIATION OF TIME OF GELATION WITH POLYMER CONCENTRATION FOR SAMPLES OF POLYVINYLCHLORIDE OF DIFFERENT MOLECULAR WEIGHT IN ETHYL BENZOATE SOLUTION

tion, then it too would be exothermic to the extent of 2-3 kcal. mole^{-1}. Thus the two reactions would be energetically competitive. Differences in frequency factors and in the dependence on concentration, however, lead to the dehydrochlorination reaction being faster under the conditions studied by the author[23].

The addition of up to 4 per cent azo-bis-isobutyronitrile to solutions of polyvinylchloride in ethyl benzoate at about 200°C. had no effect upon the time for gelation, although it increased the dehydrochlorination reaction rate. Larger amounts increased the time for gelation, and so apparently lowered the rate of cross-linking. It seems probable, however, that the initiator gave rise to chain scission reactions following chain transfer reactions with the polymer. The presence of oxygen also increased the time for gelation, presumably for a similar reason. These results again tend to support a non-radical mechanism for the cross-linking reaction.

Accordingly, it is clear that polymer degradation in solution offers a number of advantages over bulk degradation of film or powdered polymer. However, it is also clear from recent results obtained by Varma[13] that the rate of dehydrochlorination is affected by the solvent used. Three-fold differences in rates have been observed using tritolyl phosphate and dichloronaphthalene and activation energies have been found to vary as much as 5-10 kcal. mole[-1] for different solvents. Such systems need further study to elucidate the part played by the solvent.

To conclude, there is considerable evidence to support the view that dehydrochlorination proceeds *via* allyl type activation, leading to conjugated polyene structures. The precise mechanism of the process, however, is still not known. There is evidence both for and against a free radical type mechanism and further work will be necessary to decide the matter. The cross-linking reaction appears to proceed by a completely independent process, and from the limited evidence available, it seems reasonable to conclude that it is a random intermolecular condensation process.

REFERENCES

1. D. Druesedow and C. F. Gibbs, *Modern Plastics*, 1953, **30**, (10), 123.
2. E. J. Arlman, *J. Polymer Sci.*, 1954, **12**, 543.
3. K. W. Hamer, R. Kuhn, A. Smakala and K. H. Kreuchen, *Z. Physik. Chem.*, 1935, **B.29**, 363.
4. D. E. Winkler, *J. Polymer Sci.*, 1959, **35**, 3.
5. B. Baum and L. H. Wartman, *J. Polymer Sci.*, 1958, **28**, 537.
6. W. I. Bengough and R. G. W. Norrish, *Proc. Roy. Soc.*, 1950, **A 200**, 301.
7. R. R. Stromberg, S. Straus and B. G. Achhammer, *J. Res. Nat. Bur. Standards*, 1958, **60**, 147.
8. R. R. Stromberg, S. Straus and B. G. Achhammer, *J. Polymer Sci.*, 1959, **35**, 355.
9. N. Grassie, *Chem. and Ind.*, 1954, 161.
10. A. Hartmann, *Kolloid Z.*, 1954, **139**, 146.
11. G. Talamini and G. Pezzin, *Makromol Chem.*, 1960, **39**, 26.
12. W. I. Bengough and H. M. Sharpe, *Makromol Chem.*, 1963, **66**, 31.
13. W. I. Bengough and I. Varma (unpublished results).
14. A. S. Kenyon, Polymer Degradation Mechanisms, *Nat. Bur. Standards Circular*, 1958, No. 525, Nov. 16, 81.
15. A. A. Miller, *J. Phys. Chem.*, 1959, **63**, 1755.
16. B. R. Loy, *J. Polymer Sci.*, 1961, **50**, 245.
17. B. R. Loy, *J. Polymer Sci.*, 1960, **44**, 341.
18. G. J. Atchison, *J. Appl. Polymer Sci.*, 1963, **7**, 1471.
19. P. J. Flory, "Principles of Polymer Chemistry", Cornell Univ. Press, New York, 1953, p. 338, *et seq.*
20. P. J. Flory, *J. Amer.Chem. Soc.*, 1941, **63**, 3083, 3091, 3096.
21. W. H. Stockmayer, *J. Chem. Phys.*, 1943, **11**, 45.
22. W. H. Stockmayer, *J. Chem. Phys.*, 1944, **12**, 125.
23. W. I. Bengough and H. M. Sharpe, *Makromol Chem.*, 1963, **66**, 45.

CHAPTER 6

Degradation and Weathering of Polystyrene and Styrenated Polyester Resins

by C. B. BUCKNALL

DURING MANUFACTURE, fabrication and use, styrene polymers are exposed to heat, light, oxygen and mechanical shear. The results of exposure depend not only upon the conditions but also upon the nature of the polymer. The most important rigid polymers containing styrene are polystyrene (both crystal and toughened), poly(styrene-co-acrylonitrile), ABS polymers, and styrene-based polyester resins, and of these only the polyester resins are suitable for continuous outdoor use. The others become yellow and brittle within a period of months. This is perhaps the most serious limitation of these materials, the toughened grades being particularly susceptible and these must be protected by an antioxidant even for indoor applications.

Thermal Degradation of Polystyrene

The thermal degradation of polystyrene in an inert atmosphere[1] begins at about 280°C, at which temperature the molecular weight begins to fall and volatile products are evolved. As shown in Fig. 30, the fall in molecular weight at 325°C takes place in two stages, the first much more rapid than the second[2,3,4,5]. Finally at about 400°C, only a small amount of a non-volatile residue remains. The loss of volatile matter with increasing temperature[6] is illustrated in Fig. 31.

PRODUCTS OF DEGRADATION

The volatile products[7,8] are styrene monomer (44 per cent), dimer (22 per cent), trimer (27 per cent) and tetramer (4·4 per cent), with some toluene (1·9 per cent), carbon monoxide (0·13 per cent) and traces of the pentamer[9] and other fragments. Although the degradation will go to completion at 400°C, experiments can be carried out at temperatures up to 1,000°C by heating the sample rapidly on a filament[10-17]. As the temperature of degradation is raised from 400°C to 700°C, the molecular weight of the products falls and increasing amounts of monomer are formed. At higher

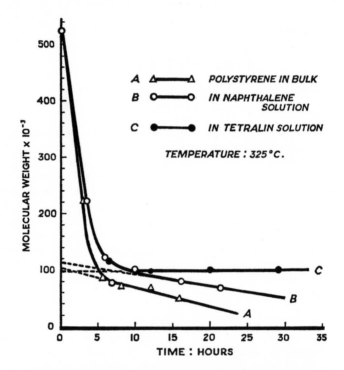

FIG. 30. CHANGE IN THE MOLECULAR WEIGHT OF POLYSTYRENE WITH TIME OF DEGRADATION AT 325°C (IN BULK AND IN SOLUTION)

temperatures a mixture of styrene, toluene, benzene, ethylene and acetylene is produced. This fall in the molecular weight of the products with increasing temperature is shown in Table 3. The conflicting results obtained by different authors show that temperature is not the only important variable. Other factors affect the composition of the product, presumably by determining the extent of secondary reactions.

TABLE 3. COMPOSITION (PERCENTAGE WEIGHT) OF PYROLYZATES OF POLY-
STYRENE DETERMINED BY CHROMATOGRAPHY[10]

Product	Temperature (°C)						
	425	525	625	725	825	1025	1125
Styrene	64·3	67·5	74·4	83·9	73·7	62·8	64·3
Ethylbenzene + toluene	Trace	Trace	Trace	0·9	2·5	5·6	5·8
Benzene	—	—	—	Trace	8·1	13·4	13·0
Acetylene	—	—	—	Trace	4·1	6·9	6·8
Ethylene	—	—	—	Trace	4·1	6·9	6·8
Carbon dioxide	—	—	—	—	—	Trace	—
Material retained in column	35·7	32·5	25·6	14·4	7·5	4·3	3·3

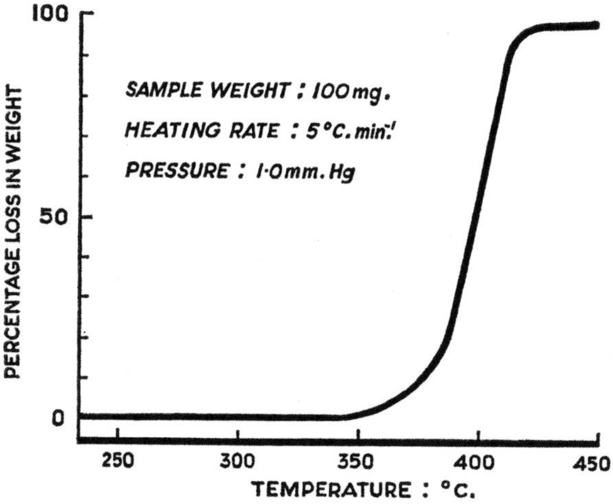

FIG. 31. THERMOGRAVIMETRIC CURVE FOR DEGRADATION
OF POLYSTYRENE[6]

The primary degradation products undergo secondary reactions both in the bulk phase, as they diffuse through the sample,
and in the vapour phase. The rate of escape of primary products
from the hot zone, and hence the extent of secondary reactions,
depends upon the thickness of the sample and upon the pressure
and flow rate[10] of the surrounding gas. Tables 4 and 5 show how
these factors affect the composition of the final products.

WEAK LINKS

Grassie and his co-workers have shown that the initial rapid
fall in molecular weight which occurs is due to the rupture of
weak links, which are formed during polymerization in a reaction
which occurs once in approximately 2,000 propagation steps[18].

They found that a similar fall in molecular weight takes place on ozonolysis[19] and that thermal chain scission proceeds at the same initial rate in the radical-acceptor tetralin as in the bulk polymer, although this solvent completely inhibits both the evolution of volatiles and the second stage of degradation, as shown in Fig. 30. From this evidence they concluded that weak links are associated with unsaturation of the main polystyrene chain and that scission takes place by a non-radical mechanism. Cameron and Grassie[19] suggested that the unsaturated structures are formed by reaction of the polystyryl radical in its resonance form:

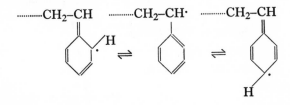

Chain scission could then proceed by the following non-radical, electron-shift mechanism:

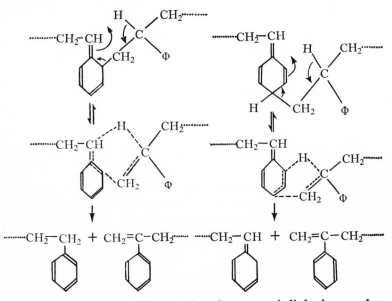

This first stage of degradation due to weak links is complete at 25 per cent volatilization[1].

TABLE 4. EFFECT OF SAMPLE SIZE ON THE COMPOSITION OF THE DEGRADATION PRODUCTS OF POLYSTYRENE[12]

Sample size (micrograms)	... 200–300	... 20–30
Monomer yield (%)	90	... 100
Pyrolysis temperature[11] (°C.) ...	about 500°C.	

TABLE 5. EFFECT OF AMBIENT PRESSURE ON THE COMPOSITION OF THE DEGRADATION PRODUCT OF POLYSTYRENE[16,17]

Pressure (mm Hg)	Pyrolysis Temp. (°C)	Heating Time	Amount of Volatilization (%)	Composition of Volatiles (%) Solid	Liquid
10^{-5} ...	362	... 1 hr. ...	83	... 57	43
760 (He) ...	362	... 1 hr. ...	83	... 45	55
10^{-5} ...	850	... 35 sec. ...	100	... 32	68
760 (He) ...	850	... 35 sec. ...	98	... 28	72

RADICAL DEPOLYMERIZATION

Depolymerization, on the other hand, is inhibited by tetralin and must therefore be a radical reaction. Experiments with deuterated polystyrene[3] show that the dimer, trimer, tetramer and pentamer are produced by a transfer reaction involving the reactive alpha hydrogen atoms: poly-α-deuterostyrene gives a 70 per cent yield of monomer, compared with 40 per cent for polystyrene and poly-β-deuterostyrene. If this transfer were intermolecular, the initial rate of degradation would be lower in tetralin solution than in bulk. As this is not the case, it is assumed that dimer formation is due to intramolecular transfer:

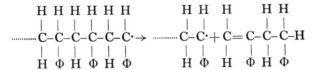

The reaction is terminated by the combination or disproportionation of pairs of radicals. Shorter polystyrene chains are formed and the molecular weight slowly falls to zero, as shown by the lower curve in Fig. 30.

REACTION KINETICS

Zero order kinetics are observed for at least part of the depolymerization reaction at low temperatures[2,6,20,21]. At higher temperatures, the order of reaction approaches unity[21,22]. Estimates of the activation energy[2,6,21] vary between 44 and 60 kcal. mole[-1], and it has been suggested[6] that this also depends on temperature and conversion.

Thermal Oxidation of Polystyrene

Polystyrene ignites in air at about 245 °C[23], burning relatively slowly with the sooty yellow flame characteristic of aromatic compounds. Self-extinguishing grades can be produced by the use of additives, particularly chlorine or bromine compounds[24].

Between about 110 °C and the ignition point, slow autoxidation takes place. Oxygen is absorbed[25] with an activation energy of 25 kcal. mole^{-1}, the molecular weight falls, carbonyl and hydroxyl bands appear in the infra-red spectrum, and small amounts of water, carbon monoxide, carbon dioxide, acetone and benzaldehyde are formed[26]. Jellinek[27] has suggested that benzaldehyde and other products act as inhibitors of the degradation.

The main infra-red band, at 5·95 microns, indicates a ketone group with perhaps some aldehyde or acid. Secondary reactions of these groups give a band at 5·75 microns, probably due to anhydrides, esters or peroxides. Weak bands also appear at 2·9 and 8·5 microns, indicating hydroxy or ether linkages[25].

The energy of activation for the formation of the 5·95 micron band is 46 kcal. mole^{-1}. The reaction has an induction period, which can. be used as a measure of reactivity. The relative reactivities of deuterated polystyrene show that the rate-controlling step is hydrogen abstraction, and that both α and β hydrogen are involved:

Repeating group in polymer:

  –CHΦCH$_2$– –CDΦCDH– –CHΦCD$_2$– –CDΦCH$_2$– –CDΦCD$_2$–

Reactivity:

    1·00   0·80   0·33   0·14   0·05

These observations are consistent with the formation and decomposition of a hydroperoxide intermediate:

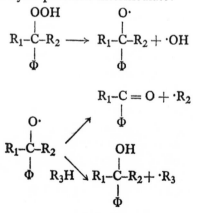

The formation of such an intermediate has been demonstrated by oxidizing polystyrene in cumene solution[28]; the polymer obtained on precipitation was capable of initiating polymerization of methylmethacrylate to give a graft copolymer.

Autoxidation proceeds much more slowly in polystyrene than in the model compound isopropylbenzene or in poly-*p*-isopropylstyrene; the polymer chain must therefore hinder hydrogen abstraction. Three explanations of this effect have been advanced:

1. The alpha hydrogen atoms are shielded by the bulky polymer chains[28].

2. Neighbouring phenyl groups are twisted owing to mutual steric repulsion, so that the reaction intermediate formed during hydrogen abstraction has reduced resonance stability[28].

3. The transition from tetrahedral to planar configuration during hydrogen abstraction is hindered by the weight of the polymer chain[29].

Photo-oxidation of Polystyrene

When polystyrene is exposed out of doors, a photo-oxidation reaction due to u.v light results in a yellowing of the polymer and a deterioration in mechanical properties. The reaction is accelerated by traces of monomer and sulphur compounds[30]. In natural sunlight the greatest damage is caused by radiation of wavelength $318 \cdot 5$ mμ.[31] Other effects include the appearance of a yellow-green fluorescence[31], the formation of infra-red bands corresponding to carbonyl and hydroxyl groups[32], the evolution of water, carbon dioxide, ethyl alcohol and other gases, and cross-linking and chain scission in the polymer[26]. In benzene solution, the quantum yield, defined as the number of links broken per quantum absorbed, is $1 \cdot 7 \times 10^{-5}$ for light of wavelength $253 \cdot 75$ mμ[14,33].

Yellowing is confined to the surface facing the light, the yellow compounds formed on first exposure absorbing u.v light and so protecting the interior. Tryon and Wall followed the reaction by measuring the absorbance at 340 mμ. As shown in Fig. 32, they found that the rate is halved by deuteration in the alpha position but hardly affected by deuteration in the beta position[34,35]. In contrast with thermal oxidation, therefore, the rate controlling step in photo-oxidation is hydrogen abstraction specifically from the alpha position.

The transmittance at 340 mμ continues to decrease after irradiation has stopped[34-37], but the change is reversed when the specimen is re-irradiated. The results of alternate irradiation and storage are illustrated in Fig. 33. The post-irradiation reaction appears to comprise two first-order reactions taking place at widely different rates. The fast reaction is presumably the decomposition of hydroperoxides, which are known to be present[35] because of their ability to initiate polymerization of methylmethacrylate. Tryon and Wall[35-37] suggest that the slow reaction is cis-trans isomerization of an acetophenone formed by the decomposition of the hydroperoxide.

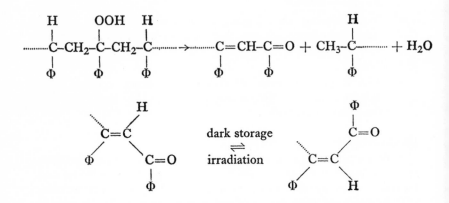

This compound would be very susceptible to oxidation and cannot account for the permanent yellowing of polystyrene, which may be due to quinoid structures[32,38].

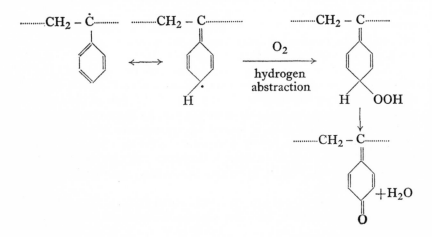

Mechanical Degradation of Polystyrene

Chain scission can be brought about by mechanical forces in the rigid, solution or rubber states. Baramboim[39] studied the degradation of solid polystyrene containing 5 per cent of a radical acceptor by cooling the polymer with liquid nitrogen and pulver-

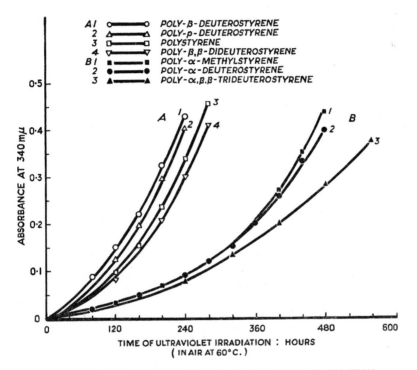

FIG. 32. EFFECT OF EXPOSURE TO ULTRA-VIOLET IRRADIATION ON THE LIGHT ABSORBANCE OF DEUTERATED POLYSTYRENES

Absorbance at 340 mμ corrected for absorbance of original polymer film

izing it in a vibrating mill. It was found that linear products are formed and that the efficiency of the acceptor is related to its activity towards peroxy radicals.

Vershinina and Kuvshinskii[40] have shown that the degree of degradation during cutting of rigid polystyrene depends upon the thickness of the shaving, the rate of cutting and the molecular weight of the polymer. Degradation is a time-dependent process taking place in layers of considerable thickness below the exposed surfaces.

In dilute solution, the maximum degradation is obtained in poor solvents, at low temperatures and at high shear rates[41]. In the rubbery state, low temperatures and high shear rates also increase the amount of degradation[42,43], while at high temperatures or low shear rates, the stress is relieved by flow rather than by chain scission. The radicals formed show little tendency to recombine and radical acceptors, such as oxygen or thio-beta-naphthol, have

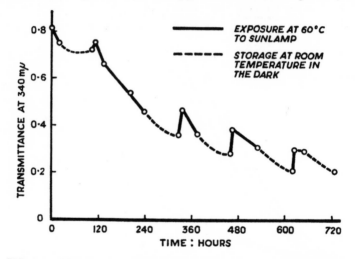

FIG. 33. EFFECT OF EXPOSURE TO ULTRA-VIOLET LIGHT AND OF SUBSEQUENT STORAGE IN THE DARK ON THE TRANSMITTANCE OF A POLYSTYRENE FILM

only a minor effect on the degradation. The limiting molecular weight reached on prolonged mastication is independent of the initial molecular weight of the polymer.

Styrene-acrylonitrile Copolymer

Like polystyrene, standard styrene-acrylonitrile copolymer containing 23 per cent acrylonitrile can be heated for an hour in vacuum at 200 °C without any colour change[44]. On heating in air, however, the copolymer undergoes the same changes as the homopolymer, but at a reduced rate[45]. The molecular weight falls—rapidly at first and then more slowly—a yellow colour forms, and bands appear in the infra-red spectrum at 5·95, 5·75, 2·9 and 8·5 microns. The rate of formation of these bands is from one-third to one-half that in the homopolymer.

It is clear from these results that the acrylonitrile component plays little part in the degradation. Grassie[46] has shown that conjugated $>C = N -$ groups are responsible for colour formation in polyacrylonitrile.

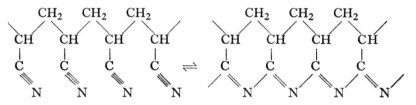

However, the concentration of $- C \equiv N$ groups in the copolymer is unaffected by heating when the styrene content is greater than 50 per cent.

Photo-oxidation also follows the same course in the copolymer as in polystyrene. The surface facing the light turns yellow, the molecular weight falls, and an absorption band at 5·9 microns indicates the formation of carboxyl groups[47]. The presence of 28 per cent by weight of acrylonitrile appears to have little effect upon the photo-degradation.

Toughened Polystyrene and ABS Polymers

Over half the total production of polystyrene is rubber modified, *i.e.*, the polystyrene contains a minor proportion of a butadiene rubber in the form of particles about 5 microns in diameter. In ABS polymer, the particle size is about 1 micron. This rubber is much more susceptible to oxidation than is polystyrene.

In an inert atmosphere, toughened polystyrene can be heated at 260°C for 20 hours without any colour change or deterioration in mechanical properties. Guiffria, Carhart and Davis[48] report a permanent increase in the refractive index of both phases, with a consequent approach to optical homogeneity.

In air, on the other hand, both heat and u.v. light cause yellowing and embrittlement, the yellow colour being due mainly to oxidation of the rubber. The penetration of oxygen into the interior increases with time[48], but the fracture resistance of the material falls as soon as the surface has been attacked. In a notched impact test, therefore, it is necessary to cut the notch before exposing the specimen. In light-aging trials, the notch must be placed facing the light.

The condition of the surface is most important in the fracture of rubber-modified materials. Table 6 shows that a single thin coating of general purpose (unmodified) polystyrene reduces the impact strength of a sheet of toughened polystyrene quite drastically, the effect of a falling weight being greater when the sheet is struck with the glossy side facing downwards[49].

TABLE 6. DROP WEIGHT IMPACT STRENGTH IN FT. LB. OF 0·115 IN. COATED AND UNCOATED TOUGHENED POLYSTYRENE SHEET[49]

	Glossy Side down		Glossy Side up
Uncoated	33·5	...	34·6
0·001 in. polystyrene foil ...	5·7	...	22·5

Tensile stresses in toughened polystyrene are thought to be relieved by the formation of microcracks around the rubber particles at right angles to the stress, followed by buckling of the polystyrene and stretching of the rubber[50,51]. In this way, the material can undergo considerable elongation before a catastrophic crack propagates through the specimen. The energy of fracture is greatly reduced if the surface is unable to respond in this way. Instead of a large number of microcracks, a small number of major cracks is formed at low tensile strains. These cracks concentrate the stress and then propagate rapidly, causing early failure.

A similar situation arises when the rubber in the surface layer is hard and inelastic as a result of oxidation; there is nothing to prevent the initiation of major cracks at low degrees of strain. The material is further weakened by the simultaneous deterioration of the polystyrene. Impact strength, flexural strength and ultimate tensile strength all drop as soon as the surface begins to degrade.

Styrenated Polyester Resins

Polyester resins give off copious white and yellow fumes on heating in an inert atmosphere, and leave a residue of carbon. Most resins will burn in air, but non-inflammable grades are available, in many of which the phthalic acid normally used is replaced by chlorinated acids such as tetrachlorophthalic or hexachlorendomethylene tetrahydrophthalic (HET) acid[52-54].

THERMAL DEGRADATION

In a thermogravimetric degradation study of a styrenated phthalic acid—maleic acid—propylene glycol polyester, Anderson and Freeman found that weight loss takes place in two stages in argon, and in four stages in air, as seen from the peaks in the curves in Fig. 34. The kinetics are summarized in Table 7.

TABLE 7. KINETIC PARAMETERS FOR THERMAL DEGRADATION OF A
STYRENATED POLYESTER[55]

Atmosphere		Stage of Reaction		Temp. Range (°C)		Order of Reaction		Activation Energy (kcal. mole⁻¹)
Air	...	I	...	200–260	...	0·4	...	19
Air	...	2,3	...	260–450	...	1·2	...	35
Air	...	4	...	450–550	...	1·0	...	79
Argon	...	1,2	...	200–450	...	1·0	...	20

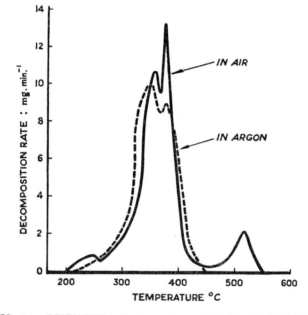

FIG. 34. DERIVATIVE THERMOGRAVIMETRIC CURVES FOR THE
THERMAL DEGRADATION OF A STYRENATED POLYESTER

The first stage of degradation in air is exothermic, and results
in the formation of benzaldehyde and unsaturated hydroxy esters.
Anderson and Freeman proposed a reaction scheme in which
the overlapping second and third stages in air are more endothermic than the corresponding first and second stages in argon.
The products of reaction in air include phthalic acid, phthalic
anhydride, esters of propylene glycol, and a non-condensable
gas comprising carbon dioxide (67 per cent), hydrogen (20 per
cent), methane (7·4 per cent) and propylene (3·4 per cent). A

fourth, exothermic stage occurs in air only, presumably as a result of oxidation of the carbonaceous residue.

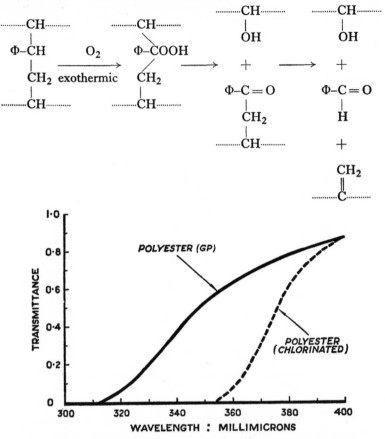

FIG. 35. ULTRA-VIOLET TRANSMISSION SPECTRA OF POLYESTER RESINS (THICKNESS 0·05 IN)

PHOTO-OXIDATION

The resistance of a styrenated polyester resin to weathering depends upon a number of factors, including the chemical composition and molecular weight of the polyester, the degree of cure, the types of initiator and accelerator used, and the presence or absence of glass fibres[56-58]. Glass-reinforced resins suffer fibre exposure as a result of dimensional changes in the resin which are not matched by the glass. Both water absorption and thermal expansion can cause fatigue failure in this way.

In addition to the effects of moisture and fluctuating temperature, polyester resins are susceptible to photo-oxidation[31,59,60]. Maximum yellowing in natural sunlight is produced by radiation of wavelength 325–330mμ, virtually identical results being obtained from resins containing adipic, phthalic or succinic acid[59]. The chlorinated self-extinguishing grades are more susceptible to photo-oxidation because of their greater absorption in the ultra-violet[53], as shown in Fig. 35.

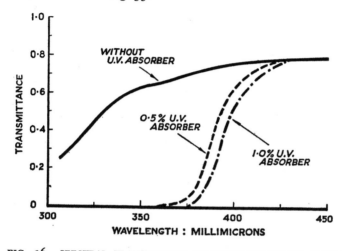

FIG. 36. SPECTRAL TRANSMISSION OF CLEAR POLYESTER SHEET
CONTAINING VARIOUS CONCENTRATIONS OF A BENZOPHENONE
U.V. ABSORBER

(Thickness of sheet—0·05 in.)

Little is known about the mechanism of photo-oxidation. Like polystyrene, polyesters give a yellow-green fluorescence after a short exposure to radiation[31], and experiments with resins of different compositions suggest that the styrene group is the main point of attack[56,57], but degradation appears to be due mainly to light absorbed by ketone groups[59,60], for the wavelength producing maximum yellowing corresponds not to maximum absorption by the resin but to maximum energy absorption by acetone[59].

A post-irradiation effect has been reported by Hirt, Schmitt and Dutton[59], the absorbance at 435·8 mμ decreasing during storage in the dark.

Polyesters are more resistant to yellowing than is polystyrene, presumably because they contain less than 50 per cent styrene, and because each cross-link comprises only one or two styrene units and thus there are no long polystyrene chains.

Degradation and Stabilization in Practice

Problems of thermal oxidation arise at all stages of the manufacture and fabrication of styrene polymers. For example, when ABS is produced by emulsion polymerization of styrene and acrylonitrile in the presence of polybutadiene, using an iron or cobalt salt with a reducing sugar to activate the peroxide initiator,

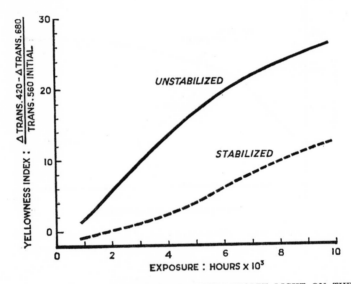

FIG. 37. EFFECT OF EXPOSURE TO ULTRA-VIOLET LIGHT ON THE COLOUR OF LIGHT-STABILIZED AND UNSTABILIZED POLYSTYRENE

it is practically impossible to remove the last traces of the metal from the finished polymer on a commercial scale. Both metals are known to catalyze the oxidation of ABS, and it is therefore necessary to protect the polymer during the drying by adding one per cent of an antioxidant to the latex before coagulation. After washing, the polymer can then be dried in an air oven at 60°C without deterioration in colour or mechanical properties.

Very high standards are demanded from fabricated articles, and small areas of slight discolouration are sufficient to spoil an extruded or moulded product. In the extrusion of high-impact polystyrene sheet, discolouration may arise both inside the extruder and after emergence from it. Discoloured material from the walls of the manifold or coupling piece between the die and the extruder is normally guided by the distributor bar to the edge of the sheet, which may then be trimmed off. Good die design and careful control of operating conditions are necessary to ensure that none of this material, which may have been held at 200 °C for over an hour, reaches the central portion of the sheet. Degradation also occurs

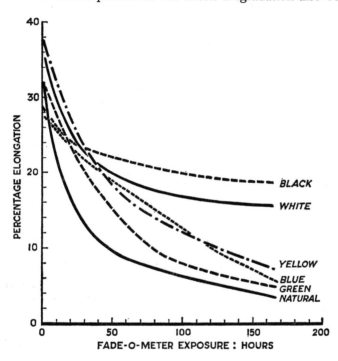

FIG. 38. CHANGE IN THE ELONGATION AT BREAK OF NATURAL AND PIGMENTED TOUGHENED POLYSTYRENE AFTER AGING

on the outside of the die, as a result of the leaks which eventually develop in most sheet extrusion dies. Barriers are generally used to prevent degraded polymer from running on to the sheet.

Injection moulding involves higher temperatures (up to 260 °C in high-speed moulding) but much shorter times. Again, there is a danger of degradation if the material is delayed in its passage through the hot zones. This can be avoided by correct design and operation of the machine.

Susceptibility to photo-oxidation[61] limits the outdoor use of polystyrene, and to a lesser extent poly(styrene-co-acrylonitrile), but excellent mouldability and low cost have made u.v. stabilized polystyrene a competitor with polymethylmethacrylate for the manufacture of fluorescent-lighting fixtures[62,63]. The u.v. absorber is added to the polymer at the colouring stage at a concentration of about 0·25 per cent. Figs. 36 and 37 show how these absorbers intercept harmful radiation and so prolong the life of the product.

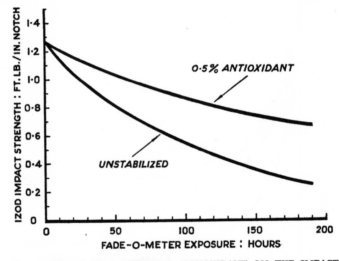

FIG. 39 EFFECT OF A PHENOLIC ANTIOXIDANT ON THE IMPACT STRENGTH OF TOUGHENED POLYSTYRENE SUBJECTED TO ACCELERATED AGING

Except for such specialized applications, stabilizers and antioxidants are not added to general-purpose polystyrene. Toughened grades, on the other hand, must be protected even for general indoor use. Colourants give some protection by absorbing or reflecting harmful radiation[64] but it is necessary to add about 0·5 per cent of a phenolic antioxidant, usually at the colouring stage, to render the toughened polymer fully serviceable. Figs. 38 and 39 show how the addition of colours and antioxidants to toughened polystyrene reduces the rate of deterioration of mechanical properties during aging.

The timing of the addition is sometimes important. In the mechanical blending process for toughening polystyrene, antioxidants can spoil the product by inhibiting cross-linking in the rubber and so preventing its dispersion as small particles. A satisfactory material is obtained if the antioxidant is added after the rubber has been cross-linked and dispersed[65].

As stated above, cross-linked polyesters are more resistant than polystyrene to photo-oxidation[66]. In roofing, fencing, greenhouses, boats, cars and many other applications, they are exposed to every extreme of weather. They are stabilized against yellowing by about o·25 per cent of a benzotriazole or hydroxy-benzophenone

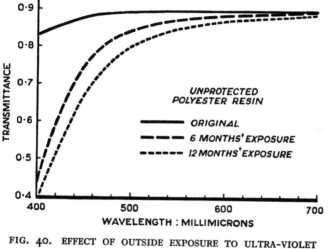

FIG. 40. EFFECT OF OUTSIDE EXPOSURE TO ULTRA-VIOLET LIGHT ON THE SPECIAL TRANSMISSION OF CLEAR UNPROTECTED POLYESTER RESIN

u.v. absorber, which is dissolved in the styrene monomer before it is added to the resin[67]. The absorber imparts a slight yellow tinge to the polyester, but preserves over a long periods the light transmission characteristics[68,69,70] which are important in many polyester applications. The transmission spectra of stabilized and unstabilized polystyrene during aging trials are compared in Figs. 40 and 41.

The Choice of a Stabilizer

The choice of an antioxidant is often determined by factors other than the degree of protection conferred. Toughened polystyrene is widely used for packaging food, and it is important that any substance added to the polymer be proved non-toxic. Also, the additive should not impart any taste or smell to the food.

The toxic hazard of an antioxidant is a function both of its inherent toxicity and of its extractability in service. In the United States, the Federal Food and Drug Administration controls the use of additives in plastics for food applications. There is no direct legislation concerning plastics in Britain, but the Ministry of Agriculture, Fisheries and Food issues a list of approved antioxidants, specifying maximum quantities permitted in foodstuffs[70]

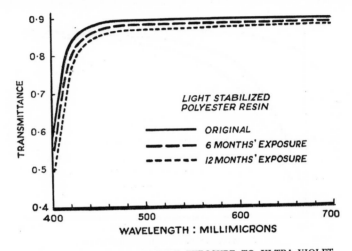

FIG. 41. EFFECT OF OUTSIDE EXPOSURE TO ULTRA-VIOLET
LIGHT ON THE SPECTRAL TRANSMISSION OF CLEAR
LIGHT-STABILIZED POLYESTER RESIN CONTAINING 0·25 PER CENT
2-HYDROXY-4-METHOXY-BENZOPHENONE

and the British Plastics Federation advises manufacturers on extraction tests and feeding trials[71].

The final choice of additives will, of course, depend on costs. The prices of non-staining antioxidants are between five shillings and fifteen shillings a pound, but the more expensive compounds generally give better protection at a given concentration. Antioxidants add roughly a half-penny per pound to the price of toughened polystyrenes.

Ultra-violet absorbers, costing from 35 shillings to 70 shillings a pound, add about three half-pence per pound to the price of the polymer. Benzotriazoles are more expensive than many hydroxybenzophenones, but again higher prices are compensated by greater efficiency, as shown in Fig. 42, and there is little to choose between the two types of compound when comparison is made on a cost-for-performance basis.

The plastics industry is only a small user of non-staining antioxidants, the rubber industry consuming most of that produced. On the other hand, nearly 40 per cent of the total production of hydroxy-benzophenones and benzotriazoles is used in polyesters, while a further 6 per cent is incorporated into polystyrene[73].

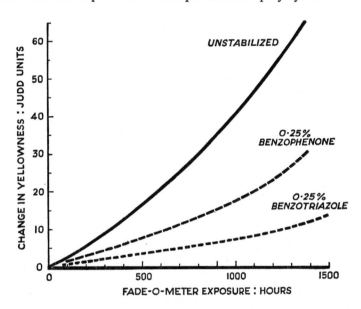

FIG. 42. EFFECT OF STANDARD COMMERCIAL LIGHT STABILIZERS ON THE YELLOWING OF CRYSTAL POLYSTYRENE SUBJECTED TO ACCELERATED AGING[72]

NOTE:—The human eye can just distinguish a change of one-third of a Judd unit

REFERENCES

1. N. Grassie and W. W. Kerr, *Internat. Symp. Makromol*, Wiesbaden, Oct., 1959, Paper III, B II.
2. H. H. G. Jellinek, *J. Polymer Sci.*, 1949, **4**, 13.
3. L. A. Wall, D. W. Brown and V. E. Hart, *J. Polymer Sci.*, 1955, **15**, 157.
4. N. Grassie and W. W. Kerr, *Trans. Faraday Soc.*, 1957, **53**, 234.
5. G. G. Cameron and N. Grassie, *Polymer*, 1961, **2**, 367.
6. D. A. Anderson and E. S. Freeman, *J. Polymer Sci.*, 1961, **54**, 253.
7. H. Staudinger and A. Steinhofer, *Ann.*, 1935, **517**, 35.
8. S. L. Madorsky and S. Straus, *Ind. Eng. Chem.*, 1948, **40**, 848, *J. Res. Nat. Bur. Std.* 1948, **40**, 417.

9. P. Bradt, V. H. Dibeler, and F. L. Mohler, *J. Res. Nat. Bur. Std.*, 1953, **50**, 201.
10. F. A. Lehmann and G. M. Brauer, *Anal. Chem.*, 1961, **33**, 673.
11. C. E. Roland Jones and A. F. Moyles, *Nature*, 1961, **189**, 222.
12. C. E. Roland Jones and A. F. Moyles, *Nature*, 1961, **191**, 663.
13. A. Barlow, R. S. Lehrle and J. C. Robb, *Polymer*, 1961, **2**, 27.
14. F. A. Lehmann, A. F. Forziati and G. M. Brauer, *Nat. Bur. Std. Ann. Rept.*, 1960, 6853.
15. H. H. G. Jellinek, *Pure and Appl. Chem.*, 1962, **4**, 419.
16. S. L. Madorsky and S. Straus, *J. Res. Nat. Bur. Std.*, 1959, **63A**, 261.
17. S. L. Madorsky, *S.P.E. Journ.*, 1961, **17**, 665.
18. N. Grassie and W. W. Kerr, *Trans. Faraday Soc.*, 1959, **55**, 1050.
19. G. G. Cameron and N. Grassie, *Makromol. Chem.*, 1962, **53**, 72.
20. S. L. Madorsky, D. McIntyre, J. H. O'Mara and S. Straus, *J. Res. Nat. Bur. Std.*, 1962, **66A**, 307.
21. S. L. Madorsky, *S.P.E. Journ.*, 1962, **18**, 1482.
22. S. L. Madorksy, *J. Polymer Sci.*, 1952, **9**, 133.
23. E. M. Schoenborn and D. S. Weaver, *A.S.T.M. Bulletin, No.* 146, May, 1947, 80.
24. Brit. Pat. 918,440; U.S. Pat. 3,063,954.
25. H. C. Beachell and S. P. Nemphos, *J. Polymer Sci.*, 1957, **25**, 173.
26. B. G. Achhammer, M. J. Reiney, L. A. Wall and F. W. Reinhart, *J. Polymer Sci.*, 1952, **8**, 555.
27. H. H. G. Jellinek in R. H. Boundy and R. F. Boyer, "Styrene", Reinhold Publishing Corp., New York, 1952, p. 650.
28. D. J. Metz and R. B. Mesrobian, *J. Polymer Sci.*, 1955, **16**, 345.
29. A. N. Pravednikov, *S.C.I. Monograph*, No. 13, 1961, 158.
30. L. A. Matheson and R. F. Boyer, *Ind. Eng. Chem.*, 1952, **44**, 867.
31. R. C. Hirt, N. Z. Searle and R. G. Schmitt, *S.P.E. Trans.*, 1961, **1**, 21.
32. B. G. Achhammer, M. J. Reiney and F. W. Reinhart, *J. Res. Nat. Bur. Std.*, 1951, **47**, 116.
33. Shih-Wei Chin, *J. Phys. Colloid Chem.*, 1949, **53**, 486.
34. M. Tryon and L. A. Wall, *J. Phys. Chem.*, 1958, **62**, 697.
35. M. Tryon and L. A. Wall in W. O. Lundberg, "Antioxidation and Antioxidants", Interscience Publishers, New York, 1962, Vol. **II**, p. 919
36. M. Tryon and L. A. Wall, *Nature*, 1956, **178**, 101.
37. L. A. Wall and M. R. Harvey and M. Tryon, *J. Phys. Chem.*, 1956, **60**, 1306.
38. N. Grassie, "Chemistry of High Polymer Degradation Processes", Butterworth, London, 1956, p. 239.
39. N. K. Baramboim, *Vysokomolekul Soedin*, 1962, **4**, 109.   *Polymer Sci.*, U.S.S.R., English transl., 1963, **4**, 41.
40. M. P. Vershinina and E. V. Kuvshinskii, *Vysokomolekul. Soedin.*, 1960, **2**, 1486. *Polymer Sci.* U.S.S.R., English Transl., 1962, **3**, 382.
41. W. R. Johnson and C. C. Price, *J. Polymer Sci.*, 1960, **45**, 217.
42. R. J. Ceresa and W. F. Watson, *J. Appl. Polymer Sci.*, 1959, **1**, 101.
43. D. J. Angier, R. J. Ceresa and W. F. Watson, *Chem. Ind., London*, 1958, 593.
44. J. A. Horrocks, to be published.
45. E. I Kirillova, E. N. Matvoeva, L. D. Zavitaeva, G. P. Fratkina and N. A. Obol'Yaninova, *Plasticheskie Massy*, 1962, (8), 3. *Soviet Plastics*, English Transl., 1962 (8), 4.
46. N. Grassie and J. N. Hay, *Soc. Chem. Ind. Monograph*, No. 13, 1961, 184.
47. E. I. Kirillova, E. N. Matveeva, K. A. Leitman, and G. P. Fratkina, *Plasticheskie Massy*, 1962 (11), 3.   *Soviet Plastics*, English Transl., 1962, (11), 4.
48. R. Giuffria, R. O. Carhart and D. A. Davis, *J. Appl. Polymer Sci.*, 1963, **7**, 1731.
49. R. O. Carhart, D. A. Davis and R. Giuffria, *S.P.E. Journ.*, 1962, **18**, 440.
50. E. H. Merz, G. C. Claver and M. Baer, *J. Polymer Sci.*, 1956, **22**, 325.
51. J. A. Schmitt and H. Keskkula, *J. Appl. Polymer Sci.*, 1960, **3**, 132.

52. C. W. Roberts, *S.P.E. Trans.*, 1963, **3,** 111.
53. C. P. Vale, *Chem. Ind., London*, 1961, 268.
54. B. Parkyn, *Brit. Plastics.*, 1959, **32,** 29.
55. D. A. Anderson and E. S. Freeman, *J. Appl. Polymer Sci.*, 1959, **1,** 192.
56. A. L. Smith and J. R. Lowry, *Plastics Technol.*, 1959, **5** (6), 42.
57. A. L. Smith and J. R. Lowry, *Mod. Plastics*, 1958, **35** (7), 134.
58. H. V. Boenig and N. Walker, *Mod. Plastics*, 1961, **38** (6), 123.
59. R. C. Hirt, R. G. Schmitt and W. L. Dutton, *Solar Energy*, 1959, **3** (2), 19.
60. J. A. Weicksel, *Mod. Plastics Encyclopedia*, 1961, 401.
61. N. Z. Searle and R. C. Hirt, *S.P.E. Trans.*, 1962, **2,** 32.
62. P. H. Estes, E. R. Smith, P. C. Woodland and E. W. Veazey, *Mod. Plastics,* 1959, **37** (1), 134.
63. R. A. McCarthy, *Plastics Technol.*, 1958, **4** (7), 640.
64. J. A. Laird, *Brit. Plastics*, 1959, **32,** 32.
65. C. B. Bucknall, *Trans. Inst. Rubber Ind.*, 1963, **39,** 221.
66. R. T. Dean and J. P. Manasia, *Mod. Plastics*, 1955, **32** (6), 131.
67. W. S. Penn, *Rubber Plast. Weekly*, 6th January, 1962, **142,** 10.
68. R. A. Coleman and J. A. Weicksel, *Mod. Plastics*, 1959, **36** (12), 117.
69. W. S. Penn, *Rubber Plast. Weekly*, 13th January, 1962, **142,** 40.
70. "Antioxidant in Food Regulations, 1958", Her Majesty's Stationery Office,· London.
71. British Plastics Federation, Second Report of the Toxicity Sub-Committee 1962.
72. American Cyanamid Co., Technical Data Sheets.
73. Anon, *Oil, Paint, Drug Reporter*, 1959, **175** (20), 3.

CHAPTER 7

Degradation of Polyolefins

by J. M. HEAPS and A. AUSTIN

THE ELECTRICAL AND MECHANICAL PROPERTIES of polyolefins, combined with their comparatively low price, make them suitable for a wide range of applications. Some indication of their importance is given by the fact that 198,000 tons were produced in the United Kingdom alone[1] during 1963.

To a large extent the usefulness of polyolefins depends on the retention of their properties during a prolonged service life and thus studies of the factors which influence their degradation are of appreciable commercial importance. In this chapter some of the more recent work which has been carried out on the pyrolysis, thermal and photo-oxidation of polyolefins is summarized and methods of retarding degradation under service conditions described. The response to high energy radiation is also considered.

Thermal Degradation in the Absence of Oxygen

Polyolefins are relatively stable to heat in the absence of oxygen and high temperatures are necessary to cause any significant decomposition. Linear polyethylene shows little or no reaction at temperatures below 290 °C and a comparison of the volatilization rates for linear polyethylene, branched polyethylene and polypropylene at 350 °C gives values of 0·004, 0·008 and 0·069 per cent per minute, respectively[2]. Activation energies, calculated from decomposition rates, range from 60 to 68 kcal. mole^{-1} for polyethylene[3,4] and polypropylene[5,6], close to the value of 66·2 kcal. mole^{-1}, observed as the bond energy of a carbon-carbon single bond[7], suggesting that the rupture of such bonds is a rate determining process.

There is evidence that the degradation of linear polyolefins occurs by random chain scission. The degradation products of polyethylene reveal a small proportion of monomer and a high-boiling fraction which includes a wide range of molecular species.

Wall and Straus[6] found that rates of volatilization at various degrees of conversion are in agreement with those predicted on the basis of random scission[8] for linear polyolefins with branches of not more than one carbon atom. In the case of polypropylene a comparison of the molecular weight distributions before and after varying degrees of degradation again indicates random chain scission. However, it has not been possible to interpret the kinetics in terms of a simple process in which the rate of bond rupture is proportional to the number of bonds present[5].

The presence of branches of more than one carbon atom causes a change in the degradation process, and plots of degradation rate against conversion for branched polyethylene, branched polypropylene and polyisobutene indicate a non-random mechanism[6].

One effect of branching is a lowering of the thermal stability by the presence of the more reactive hydrogen atoms attached to tertiary carbon atoms and the weaker carbon-carbon bonds attached to quaternary carbon atoms. This is reflected in the higher volatilization rate of polypropylene compared with linear polyethylene and the preferred scission of such weak bonds in branched polyethylene indicated by infra-red studies[9] and the results of non-isothermal thermogravimetric analysis[10].

Such effects, however, are not sufficient to explain the change in the degradation process and Wall and Straus[6] suggest that intramolecular hydrogen transfer is sterically favoured in branched structures. Thus, after the initial chain scission, repeated transfer in the manner indicated below causes all or a large portion of a given chain to decompose into small fragments.

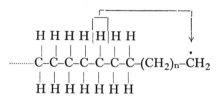

$$\cdots\cdots\cdots CH_2-CH_2-CH_2-CH_2-\overset{\bullet}{C}H-CH_2-CH_2-(CH_2)_n-CH_3$$

$$\cdots\cdots\cdots CH_2-CH_2-\overset{\bullet}{C}H_2+CH_2=CH-CH_2-CH_2-(CH_2)_n-CH_3$$

Oxidation of Polyolefins

Polyolefins readily suffer oxidation, resulting in embrittlement, darkening, and decrease in molecular weight. The formation of polar groups and cross-links will take place at a much lower temperature than that of pyrolytic decomposition and is believed to result from an autocatalytic, free-radical, degradation reaction similar to that postulated for the oxidation of low-molecular-weight hydrocarbons[11,12].

Kinetic studies of the oxidation of polyolefin melts, made by measuring the rate of oxygen uptake[13-21], by following the oxidation exotherm[22,23] and by observing the formation of polar groups by infra-red spectroscopy [22,24-26], indicate that oxidation takes place in two distinct stages. Immediately after contact with oxygen there is an induction period during which the material shows a slow rate of oxygen absorption. There is a slight rise in temperature and carbonyl and hydroperoxide compounds are formed in amounts which tend towards equilibrium concentrations. At the end of the induction period there is an abrupt transition to a stage where oxygen-uptake increases at an accelerating rate, the temperature rises explosively and there is a rapid formation of oxygen-containing groups.

Infra-red [22,24-26] and chemical analyses[27] show that hydroperoxides are the precursors of the carbonyl and hydroxyl compounds formed during oxidation and it is considered that the induction period represents the time necessary for the build-up of a sufficiently high concentration of peroxides which subsequently decompose by a free-radical mode and cause rapid oxidation[12].

The length of the induction period and the rate of subsequent oxidation depend upon availability of oxygen. Thus the induction periods observed for low density and Ziegler polyethylenes[14] are found to be inversely proportional to the square root of the oxygen pressure, the maximum rate of absorption increasing directly with the pressure. Increase in specimen thickness to the point where diffusion controls the availability of oxygen will also prolong the apparent induction period. The presence of an antioxidant in low density polyethylene prolongs the induction period by an amount directly proportional to the antioxidant concentration, oxidation proceeding at the normal rate at the end of the extended induction period[28].

Increase in temperature reduces induction periods and increases maximum oxygen absorption rates. Both these functions give linear Arrhenius plots[13-15,18,20,21] and have been used to determine apparent activation energies for the initiation and propagation stages of oxidation.

Measurement of gel fraction and viscosity of oxidized polyolefins shows that chain rupture predominates over cross-link formation in polypropylene, the tendency to cross-link increasing in the series, polypropylene, low density polyethylene, ethylene-propylene copolymer (14 mol per cent propylene), high density polyethylene[21]. In all cases, useful mechanical and electrical properties are completely lost before the end of the induction period[14,17,18].

The oxidation reaction is not significantly different below the melting point of crystalline polyolefins. However, the presence of oxygen-impermeable regions limits the extent of oxidation, and increased crystalline content has been shown to prolong the induction period and to cause a decrease in the maximum oxidation rate of polyethylene[18,28-30] and polypropylene[18]. The presence of impermeable crystalline regions is indicated by an abrupt transition from an accelerating rate of oxygen absorption to a decelerating rate. The oxygen absorption at this transition is only a fraction of that absorbed in the molten state and has been shown to be inversely proportional to the degree of crystallinity[18,28-30]. Branched polymers such as poly(3-methyl-butene-1) and poly(4-methyl-pentene-1) in which the crystalline regions have a similar density to the amorphous portion, and presumably have a similar oxygen-permeability, appear to oxidize homogeneously[30].

The belief that the readily-accessible amorphous regions are preferentially attacked is supported by infra-red studies[31], which indicate an increase in the ratio of crystalline to unoxidized amorphous material following oxidation, and by microscopic examination of oxidized samples of polypropylene[32,33] which shows the development of well defined cracks at spherulite boundaries. The latter work also reveals the presence of radial spherulitic cracks, probably resulting from internal reorganization rather than from chemical degradation.

In certain polyolefin-antioxidant systems, Arrhenius plots show a discontinuity at the crystalline melting point, oxidation proceeding with a higher activation energy in the solid state than in the melt. This has been observed with high-density polyethylene stabilized with carbon black[28,34] or pyrogallol-coated silica particles[34], and with polypropylene containing phenolic antioxidants[35], and is attributed to the exclusion of antioxidant from the crystalline regions causing an enrichment in the more vulnerable amorphous material.

Photolytic Oxidation

Whereas the thermal oxidation of polyolefins is negligible at low temperatures, exposure to ultra-violet radiation in the presence of air can initiate chain scission[36,37], crosslinking[37] and the formation of polar groups[38] at ambient temperatures.

Pross and Black[38] have shown that polyethylene has a small ultra-violet absorption at 290 to 330mμ and Melchore[39] has reported that radiation with a wave length of 300mμ is responsible for most of the degradation observed in polypropylene. Such absorption is explained by the presence of a small number of carbonyl groups, and the resulting degradation process may be attributed to free radicals produced either by the photo-decomposition of ketonic compounds or by the activation of the hydrocarbon chain adjacent to the carbonyl group. Free radicals thus formed can react with oxygen to give peroxy radicals which propagate the degradation by the normal autoxidation mechanism. However, the ultra-violet degradation of polyolefins differs from thermal oxidation in that the number of oxidation cycles per initiation step is small and the rate of initiation high[40]. Moreover, since more ketonic groups are formed as by-products of oxidation, the rate of absorption of energy tends to increase with time of irradiation[37].

Using an oxygen absorption technique, Neiman et al[41] have shown that a well-defined induction period precedes the rapid photo-oxidation of polypropylene. From the variation of this induction period with temperature, they calculated the activation energy of the initiation process to be 7 kcal. mole[-1]. Previous workers observed that the rate of the overall degradation reaction is doubled by a 10 °C increase in temperature[39].

Although the overall deterioration in mechanical properties can be blamed on a decrease in molecular weight[36], Cotten and Sacks[37] have shown that both cross-linking and scission occur simultaneously in high-density polyethylene, the incidence of cross-linking being governed by the ease of oxygen access to the reaction site. Thus increases in specimen thickness or crystallinity have been found to favour chain scission.

Catalyzed Oxidation

The presence of metallic contaminants accelerates the thermal oxidation of low-molecular-weight hydrocarbons by catalyzing the breakdown of hydroperoxides, producing a much higher concentration of radicals than does the thermal decomposition process[42]. A similar reaction is presumed to occur in polyolefins where the presence of copper or copper compounds causes a rapid acceleration of the oxidation of polypropylene[43,44]. Copper, chromium, manganese and lead compounds produce a similar effect in low-density polyethylene even in the presence of antioxidants[45]. It seems probable that catalyst residues in Ziegler polyethylene and polypropylene may produce a similar effect. However, the phenomenon is complex since individual catalyst components appear to be able to promote or hinder oxidation in the presence of anti-oxidants[46].

The effect of copper and copper compounds on the oxidation of polypropylene has been studied by Hansen *et al.*, using an oxygen absorption technique[43,44]. Their results show that 1·5 per cent copper or cupric stearate reduces the induction period by a factor of 1/3 or 1/10 respectively, the subsequent oxidation rapidly attaining the catalytic (non-accelerating) rate. The apparent activation energy for the initiation process is found to be close to that observed for the autoxidation reaction, implying that the same reaction mechanism is involved.

Antioxidant effectiveness can be largely restored by the addition of oxamide compounds[44], the most effective being oxanilide which forms a stable complex insoluble in hydrocarbon polymers. However, even the oxanilide complex appears to act as a weak oxidation catalyst.

The Effect of Structure on Oxidative Stability

The relative stability of polyolefins to oxidation is determined by the ease with which radicals can be formed and the way in which they subsequently react, and both these factors are controlled to a large extent by molecular structure.

The initiation process requires the formation of free radicals at moderate temperatures too low for the rupture of main-chain carbon-carbon bonds and is believed to depend on the presence of "weak bonds" and structural imperfections. Two types of weak link are present in polyolefins; carbon-hydrogen bonds adjacent to vinyl, vinylidene or carbonyl groups, and tertiary carbon-hydrogen bonds. The amount of unsaturation is normally small, about three double bonds per thousand carbon atoms, but it makes a significant contribution to oxidative instability[22], infra-red evidence indicating preferential attack of oxygen upon the α-carbon atom[24]. Moreover, Notley[16] considers that bonds which are adjacent to unsaturated linkages are the most likely sites for the initiation reaction.

The concentration of tertiary carbon atoms probably influences the propagation reaction more than the initiation process. Results of oxygen absorption studies on melts show that a decrease in the induction period and an increase in the maximum oxidation rate occur with increase in the degree of branching[13,21,22,25]. Matveeva and co-workers[21] arranged polyolefins in order of decreasing stability as follows: low-density polyethylene, high-density polyethylene, ethylene-propylene copolymer (15 mol. percent propylene), polypropylene; and obtained values of the activation energy calculated from rate measurements of 32·7, 31·9, 30·8, and 21·8 kcal. mole[-1] respectively. However, their ranking of low-density polyethylene (methyl content 33 per 100 carbon atoms) and high-density polyethylene (methyl content 10 per 100 carbon atoms) is the reverse of that observed by other workers[22,25].

There is some indication that the steric configuration of polyolefin molecules can influence stability to oxidation. Hawkins *et al.*[28] have observed that atactic polypropylene is only slightly inferior to isotactic polypropylene in its resistance to oxidation at 140°C, even though the former is molten at this temperature, and studies of the oxidation in solution of polypropylene and polybutene-1 showed the atactic form to have superior stability[20].

In the latter work, this difference in stability is correlated with the observation that hydroperoxide decomposition proceeds by a unimolecular mechanism in the atactic polymer and a bimolecular mechanism in the isotactic polymer. It is suggested that the isotactic configuration is sterically favourable for the interaction of a peroxy radical on a tertiary carbon atom with an adjacent tertiary carbon atom on the same chain to form a hydroperoxide and leave a hydrocarbon radical at the attacked site. This hydrocarbon radical then reacts with molecular oxygen to give a peroxy radical which can attack the next tertiary carbon atom along the chain, the process repeating zipper fashion to leave hydroperoxide groups on alternate carbon atoms. There is evidence to suggest that these are sufficiently close to allow bimolecular decomposition.

During the oxidation of atactic or syndiotactic polymers, this intramolecular process will be hindered by the less favourable arrangement of the monomer units so that hydroperoxide groups will occur statistically throughout the bulk of the material and their decomposition will be predominantly unimolecular. Since the intramolecular process will facilitate the propagation reactions, the relative instability of the isotactic polymers is satisfactorily explained.

Both initiation and propagation reactions require the ready availability of oxygen and structural features which restrict this tend to enhance stability. Thus structural regularity can result in a high crystalline/amorphous ratio which will increase resistance to oxidation at temperatures below the crystalline melting point.

It has also been shown by Hansen *et al.*[18] that the presence of bulky side groups can restrict the accessibility of tertiary carbon atoms to oxygen. They observed that polyvinylcyclohexane and poly-3-phenyl-1-propene exhibit induction periods which are respectively ten and thirty times those found for linear polyethylene under the same conditions. Smaller side groups such as those in polybutene-1 do not show this effect.

Degradation and Stabilization in Practice

Under mild conditions, unstabilized polyolefins will retain their properties for long periods and it is reported that low-density polyethylene stored for ten years in the dark at room temperature showed no change in brittle point[47]. However, in most applications, exposure to heat or light will accelerate oxidative degradation, causing initially a decrease in elongation and an increase in brittle temperature and power factor, and subsequently loss of flexibility, the development of surface cracks, discolouration and embrittlement.

To retard oxidation and prolong service life, antioxidants and light stabilizers are normally added. These can be incorporated by any of the conventional thermoplastic compounding techniques provided care is taken to ensure good dispersion, but antioxidants are normally added immediately after the purification stage in polymer manufacture so as to give protection during subsequent processing.

The effectiveness of various antioxidants in low-density polyethylene has been compared at 110° and 170°C by Baum and Perun[48] who measured the induction period to produce an arbitrary change in the infra-red absorption due to carbonyl groups at 5·84μ. This work covers more than a hundred antioxidants and some of the results are given in Table 8.

TABLE 8. EFFECTIVENESS OF ANTIOXIDANTS IN LOW-DENSITY POLYETHYLENE[48]

Antioxidant	Induction period	
	110°C. (days)	170°C. (hours)
4-tert-butyl phenol	0·5–1	0·5
2,6-di-tert-butyl-4-methyl phenol	0·5–1	0·5
Bis-(4-hydroxy phenyl) 2,2'-propane	1	0·5
Bis-(2-hydroxy-3-tert-butyl-5-methyl phenyl) methane	10	1·5
4,4'-thiobis (3-methyl-6-tert-butyl phenol)	12	1·5
p-phenylene diamine	1·5	0·5
N,N'-diphenyl p-phenylene diamine	14	3
Agerite Resin D	25	1

The choice of type and amount of antioxidant hinges to a large extent on the susceptibility of the polyolefin to oxidation, stabilizer requirements increasing in the series, high-density polyethylene, low-density polyethylene, ethylene-propylene copolymers, polypropylene. Results shown in Table 9 illustrate the increased stabilizer requirements of polypropylene compared with low-density polyethylene.

TABLE 9.   COMPARISON OF STABILIZER REQUIREMENTS

A comparison of induction periods of low-density polyethylene and polypropylene at 140°C in oxygen at a pressure of one atmosphere, using 4-4'-thiobis (3-methyl-6-tert-butyl phenol) as the antioxidant[44].

	Antioxidant concentration (%)	Induction period (hours)
l.d. polyethylene	0	4
l.d. polyethylene	0·1	1000
polypropylene	0	1–2
polypropylene	0·5	400

The need for improved antioxidants for polypropylene has been largely met by the use of mixtures of an antioxidant with certain phosphorous and sulphur compounds which synergistically enhance their stabilizing efficiency. Various compounds have been studied[35,49] and, of these, dilauryl thiodipropionate is probably the best known example. Some indication of its synergistic effect is given by the finding that, whereas 0·1 per cent of a hindered phenol or 0·3 per cent dilauryl thiodipropionate in polypropylene inhibit oxidation at 150°C for only a few hours if used separately, a combination of the two gives a composition which is stable for more than seventy days at this temperature[44].

An important factor in the effectiveness of antioxidants in practice is resistance to loss from the polymer by volatilization and extraction. Hawkins *et al.*[50] have shown that volatilization at 105°C from low-density polyethylene specimens can reduce antioxidant concentration from 0·1 to 0·01 per cent in less than two weeks. Immersion in water for less than 24 hours at 60°C halved the induction period and only carbon black and a Thiokol polymer were completely retained in these tests.

Further restriction on the choice of stabilizer can also be made by the nature of the end use. Thus, when the polymer is intended for use in contact with foodstuffs, antioxidants with acceptable non-tainting and non-toxic properties must be incorporated. Even in less exacting applications, antioxidants can exhibit undersirable side effects; for instance, diphenyl *p*-phenylene diamine shows a tendency to bloom at a concentration of 0·1 per cent and can cause staining. Moreover, amine antioxidants and, to a less extent, phenolic antioxidants can act as sensitizers for u.v. degradation[51].

Because of the high initiation rate of photo-oxidation, antioxidant systems which are satisfactory thermal stabilizers are

relatively ineffective as light stabilizers for polyolefins. It is therefore necessary to incorporate into materials likely to be exposed to
strong sunlight additives which can absorb harmful ultra-violet
radiation and dispose of the energy by non-radical-forming processes.

Pigments are the most effective ultra-violet absorbers and a
concentration of 5 per cent of various organic and inorganic pigments has been found to restrict the degradation of linear polyethylene to surface oxidation, thus increasing the time to failure,
for example, in Arizona exposure tests, from six months to more
than a year[52]. A comparison of various pigments at a 1 per cent concentration in low-density polyethylene shows red iron oxide and
carbon black to be very much more effective in preventing degradation than titanium dioxide or phthalocyanin pigments[36]. Well
dispersed, fine-particle channel black is particularly efficient
and a 1 per cent concentration has been reported to prevent the
degradation of polyethylene during twenty years of out-door exposure in Florida[53].

Channel black and, to a less extent, furnace black are also mild
antioxidants for polyethylene[54,55]. Their effectiveness increases
with concentration[55] and there is a correlation with the concentration of surface groups. However, they have a deleterious effect on
mechanical properties at concentrations greater than 5 per cent and
at this level they are not efficient stabilizers at processing temperatures[28], so that additional antioxidant may be required. Choice of
the supplementary stabilizer to be used with carbon black requires
care, since it can reduce antioxidant effectiveness[55,56], and it is
preferable to use sulphur containing compounds such as thiobis-
(4-methyl-6-tertiary-butyl phenol)[57], thiobis-(2-naphthol)[58], organic disulphides or thioethers[58] which synergistically enhance the
stabilizing action of carbon black.

When transparent or lightly coloured compositions are required, materials which absorb only in the ultra-violet region of the
spectrum must be used and organic compounds such as 2-hydroxy-
benzophenone[39,41,59] or 2-hydroxy benzotriazole[41,59] have been
used. The effectiveness of these compounds increases linearly with
concentration[41] and has been related to their ability to filter out
radiation[39] with a wavelength of 300mμ, but is also dependent on
their antioxidant properties[60].

Resistance to High Energy Radiation

While, in quantitative terms, the utilization of plastics in
radiation environments is relatively insignificant, there remains an

urgent need in marine and land-based nuclear reactors and in space satellites for insulating, shielding and moderating materials which suffer little deterioration in physical properties following moderate exposures to ionizing radiation. Polyethylene ranks intermediate among high polymers generally in resistance to radiation. It is not as inert, for example, as polystyrene and phenol-formaldehyde resins but much more durable than polymethylmethacrylate, polytetrafluoroethylene and polyformaldehyde or neoprene and other elastomers. The attractive combination of properties of this low-cost tough plastic ensures that polyethylene is the material generally specified for insulating and shielding duties in radiation environments.

The preference for polyethylene arises not so much because the material resists radiation but because of beneficial change, in that the polyethylene becomes cross-linked and gains in heat and deformation resistance. The low dielectric constant and loss factor of polyethylene are impaired by high doses of radiation[61], but the breakdown voltage may be improved. The deterioration in dielectric properties is similar to that produced by milling in air and may be attributed to radiation-induced oxidation. Polyethylene containing an efficient antioxidant suffers far less change on irradiation in air, both in electrical and mechanical properties.

The chemical changes occurring in irradiated polyethylene are quite different from those produced by pyrolysis. Whereas the latter produces mainly monomer and high boiling hydrocarbons, irradiation produces predominantly hydrogen (to the extent of 95 to 98 per cent of liberated gases) with small amounts of alkanes, arising from side-chain cleavage of branched polymer. This is coupled with the formation of cross-links and vinylene double bonds, the former accounting for the improved mechanical properties at temperatures above the crystalline melting point. When thin films of polyethylene are irradiated in oxygen, extensive degradation occurs and the formation of cross-links hardly makes itself felt. Equally, when previously irradiated and cross-linked polyethylene is exposed to oxygen at high temperatures, the density of cross-links falls.

Polypropylene and poly-n-olefins are less resistant than polyethylene to ionizing radiation. By virtue of the presence in the main chain of substituted carbon atoms, main chain scission is enhanced and a cross-linked product is difficult to achieve. Polyisobutylene which contains doubly substituted main chain carbon atoms is particularly vulnerable, suffering rapid degradation to become almost useless after only 10–20 Mrad of irradiation[62,63].

Degradation of Cross-linked Polyethylene

To ensure the minimum change in physical and electrical properties of polyethylene insulation when exposed to stratospheric radiation belts, it is preferred to irradiate the insulation first to doses higher than any they are likely to encounter when used in space vehicles. In the vacuum of outer space, this preserves the initial electrical properties virtually indefinitely, and all the U.S. satellites are allegedly wired with irradiated polythene equipment wire.

When attempts are made to exploit the non-melting character of cross-linked polyethylene in the normal atmosphere, the sensitivity to oxidative degradation assumes greater importance. In normal polyethylene applications, serious oxidation only occurs at high temperatures or on exposure to ultra-violet light. The latter can be avoided by incorporating carbon black and/or u.v. absorbers, while the former is not a practical limitation since polyethylene melts to a useless liquid before reaching temperatures where thermal oxidation is rapid. Cross-linking, however, enables polyethylene to be used theoretically at temperatures up to 300 °C, beyond which non-oxidative thermal pyrolysis makes its presence felt. Indeed, a measurable tensile strength has been observed for cross-linked polyethylene at 287 °C, but only when tested in a nitrogen atmosphere[64]. When the test was repeated in air, the strength fell to zero in a few minutes. Accordingly, the non-melting character of irradiated polyethylene can be exploited in practice only *via* the aid of antioxidants of which di- β-naphthyl-*p*-phenylene diamine is the most effective. Suitably stabilized cross-linked polyethylene has been guaranteed a service life of 1,000 hours at 150 °C[65]. Flame retarded cross-linked polyethylene suitable for use at high temperature is also available.

Though cross-linked polyethylene was first prepared by high energy irradiation, products with similar properties can be made by heat treatment in the presence of free-radical initiators such as dicumyl peroxide or 2.4-dimethyl-2.4-di-*tert*-butyl peroxyhexane. Chemical cross-linking appears a more economical process for producing insulated conductors, where the plastic is supported by the wire during high temperature cure. High loadings of carbon black have been incorporated into vulcanizable polyethylene to improve strength and heat resistance, and antioxidants and flame retardants are also commonly incorporated [66]. These measures enhance still further the status of polyethylene as a durable degradation-resistant material.

Despite suggestions of suitable techniques in the patent

literature[67], cross-linked products based on polypropylene and other polyolefins have not been introduced commercially and it must be assumed that the reduced oxidation resistance of highly branched polyolefins has proved an insurmountable obstacle.

Summary

Polyethylene may be classed as a material with poor inherent resistance to degradation and weathering, but one which can be greatly improved in this respect by the incorporation of additives. Since it is normally used at ambient temperature, far below the temperature threshold for thermal pyrolysis, its susceptibility to oxidation provides the chief ground for concern. Even oxidation proceeds at a negligible rate at low temperatures, except in the presence of ultra-violet light. The sensitivity of polyethylene to ultra-violet radiation is thought to be caused by carbonyl groups derived from the initiator or otherwise generated during polymerization and this has to be controlled in polyethylene articles designed for outdoor exposure by the incorporation of pigments and/or antioxidants, of which carbon black is the most efficacious. Carbon black-pigmented low-density polyethylene, in fact, can be guaranteed a twenty-year life which is a striking improvement over the effective outdoor life of about one year of unpigmented polyethylene.

Polypropylene and other polyolefins exhibit reduced thermal stability and increased sensitivity to oxidation due to the presence of substituted carbon atoms in the main chain. This is not necessarily reflected in a commensurate reduction in effective service life outdoors, since the higher crystallinity of polypropylene reduces access of oxygen to the vulnerable sites. Moreover, antioxidants and u.v. absorbers which concentrate in the amorphous regions are found to be most effective in reducing the photo-oxidation of polypropylene and stabilized pigmented polypropylene has a longer effective outdoor life than has similarly protected coloured polyethylene, though the extremely good performance of carbon black-filled polyethylene is not reproduced.

Polyethylene is valued for its stability in a high energy radiation environment, where its properties undergo improvement. Irradiation or chemical curing of polyethylene has led to products with form stability at temperatures above the crystalline melting point and with extremely good resistance to weathering and oxidation at elevated temperatures. Polypropylene is degraded by ionizing radiation and has not been produced commercially in cross-linked form.

REFERENCES

1. *Board of Trade Business Monitor*, Section P21, Oct.-Dec., 1963.
2. L. A. Wall, S.L. Madorsky, D. W. Brown, S. Straus and R. Simha. *J. Amer. Chem. Soc.*, 1954, **76**, 3430.
3. S. L. Madorsky and S. Straus, *J. Res. Nat. Bur. Stand.*, 1954, **53**, 361.
4. S. L. Madorsky, *J. Polymer Sci.*, 1952, **9**, 133.
5. T. E. Davis, R. L. Tobias and E. B. Peterli, *J. Polymer Sci.*, 1962, **56**, 485.
6. L. A. Wall and S. Straus, *J. Polymer Sci.*, 1960, **44**, 313.
7. T. L. Cottrell, "The Strengths of Chemical Bonds", Butterworths, London, 1954, p. 275.
8. R. Simha, *J. Chem. Phys.*, 1956, **24**, 796.
9. W. G. Oakes and R. B. Richards, *J. Chem. Soc.*, 1949, 2929.
10. D. A. Anderson and E. S. Freeman, *J. Polymer Sci.*, 1961, **54**, 253.
11. J. L. Bolland, *Proc. Roy. Soc. (Lond.)*, 1946, **186**, 218.
    J. L. Bolland and G. Gee, *Trans. Faraday Soc.*, 1946, **42**, 236.
12. A. V. Tobolsky, *Discuss. Faraday Soc.*, 1947, No. 2, 384.
13. T. H. Meltzer, J. J. Kelley and R. N. Goldey, *J. Appl. Polymer Sci.*, 1960, **3**, 84.
14. B. M. Grieveson, R. N. Haward and B. Wright, *S.C.I. Monograph*, No. 13, 1961, 413.
15. N. T. Notley, *Trans. Faraday Soc.*, 1962, **58**, 66.
16. N. T. Notley, *Trans. Faraday Soc.*, 1964, **60**, 88.
17. C. A. Russell and J. V. Pascale, *J. Appl. Polymer Sci.*, 1963, **7**, 959.
18. R. H. Hansen, W. M. Martin and T. de Benedictis, *Trans. Proc. I.R.I.*, 1963, **39**, T301.
19. G. W. Bell and C. E. Heyd, *S.P.E. Trans.*, 1964, **4**, 39.
20. L. Dulog, E. Radlmann and W. Kern, *Makromol. Chem.*, 1963, **60**, 1.
21. E. N. Matveeva, S. S. Khin'kis, A. I. Tsvetkova and V. A. Balandina, *Plasticheskie Massy*, 1963, (1), 2. English Translation in *Soviet Plastics*, 1964, (1), 4.
22. B. Baum, *J. Appl. Polymer Sci.*, 1959, **2**, 281.
23. A. Rudin, H. P. Schreiber and M. H. Waldman, *Ind. Eng. Chem.*, 1961, **53**, 137.
24. J. P. Luongo, *J. Polymer Sci.*, 1960, **42**, 139.
25. H. C. Beachell and G. W. Tarbet, *J. Polymer Sci.*, 1960, **45**, 451.
26. S. S. Stivala, L. Reich and P. G. Kelleher, *Makromol. Chem.*, 1963, **59**, 28.
27. E. Beati, F. Severini and G. Clerici, *Makromol. Chem.*, 1963, **61**, 104.
28. W. L. Hawkins, W. Matreyek and F. H. Winslow, *J. Polymer Sci.*, 1959, **41**, 1.
29. F. H. Winslow, W. L. Hawkins and W. Matreyek, *Amer. Chem. Soc., Div. Polymer Chem. Preprints*, 1961, **2**, 186.
30. F. H. Winslow, C. J. Aloisio, W. L. Hawkins, W. Matreyek and S. Matsuoka, *Chem. and Ind.*, 1963, 533.
31. J. P. Luongo, *J. Polymer Sci.*, 1963, **B1**, 141.
32. J. van Schooten, *J. Appl. Polymer Sci.*, 1960, **4**, 122.
33. M. Inoue, *J. Polymer Sci.*, 1961, **55**, 443.
34. W. L. Hawkins, W. Matreyek and F. H. Winslow, *J. Appl. Polymer Sci.* 1961, **5**, 515.
35. N. P. Neureiter and D. E. Brown, *Ind. Eng. Chem., Prod. Res. Develop.*, 1962, **1**, 236.
36. R. J. Matinovich, *S.P.E. Tech. Papers*, 1963, **9**, Session 1, Paper 1.
37. G. R. Cotten and W. Sacks, *J. Polymer Sci.*, 1963, **A1**, 1345.
38. A. W. Pross and R. M. Black, *J. Soc. Chem. Ind.*, 1950, **69**, 113.
39. J. A. Melchore, *Ind. Eng. Chem., Prod. Res. Develop.*, 1962, **1**, 232.
40. A. R. Burgess, *Nat. Bur. Stand. Circular*, 1953, No. 525, 149.
41. M. B. Neiman, V. Ya. Efremov, B. V. Rozynov and Ya. E. Vilento, *Plasticheskie Massy*, 1962, (9), 4. English translation in *Soviet Plastics*, 1962, (9), 4.

42. H. E. De La Mare, J. K. Kochi and F. F. Rust, *J. Amer. Chem. Soc.*, 1961, 83, 2013; J. K. Kochi and F. F. Rust. *J. Amer. Chem. Soc.*, 1961, 83, 2017; J. K. Kochi, *J. Amer. Chem. Soc.*, 1961, 83, 3162.
43. R. H. Hansen, T. de Benedictis and W. M. Martin, *Trans. Proc. I.R.I.*, 1963, 39, T290.
44. R. H. Hansen, C. A. Russell, T. de Benedictis, W. M. Martin and J. V. Pascale, *J. Polymer Sci.*, 1964, A2, 587.
45. H. Alter, *Ind. Eng. Chem.*, 1960, 52, 121.
46. D. Ryshavy and L. Balaban, *S.P.E. Trans.*, 1962, 2, 25.
47. V. T. Wallder, W. J. Clarke, J. B. De Coste and J. B. Howard, *Ind. Eng. Chem.*, 1950, 42, 2320.
48. B. Baum and A. L. Perun, *S.P.E. Trans.*, 1962, 2, 250.
49. M. S. Khloplyankina, A. F. Lukovnikov and P. I. Levin, *Vysokomol. Soed.*, 1963, 5, 105. English translation in *Polymer Science U.S.S.R.*, 1963, 4, 812.
50. W. L. Hawkins, M. A. Worthington and W. Matreyek, *J. Appl. Polymer Sci.*, 1960, 3, 277.
51. W. O. Lundberg, Ed., "Autoxidation and Antioxidants", Vol. II, Interscience, New York, 1962, p. 935.
52. C. Gottfried and M. J. Dutzer, *J. Appl. Polymer Sci.*, 1961, 5, 612.
53. W. L. Hawkins and F. L. Winslow, *Trans. J. Plast. Inst.*, 1961, 29, 82
54. B. S. Biggs, *Nat. Bur. Stand. Circular*, 1953, No. 525, 137.
55. W. L. Hawkins, R. H. Hansen, W. Matreyek and F. H. Winslow, *J. Appl. Polymer Sci.*, 1959, 1, 37.
56. T. R. Crompton, *J. Appl. Polymer Sci.*, 1962, 6, 558.
57. P. I. Levin, *Plasticheskie Massy*, 1962, (11), 43. English translation in *Soviet Plastics*, 1962, (11), 40.
58. W. L. Hawkins, V. L. Lanza, B. B. Loeffler, W. Matreyek and F. H. Winslow, *J. Appl. Polymer Sci.*, 1959, 1, 43.
59. A. F. Strobel and S. C. Catino, *Ind. Eng. Chem., Prod. Res. Develop.*, 1962, 1, 241.
60. J. H. Chaudet and J. W. Tamblyn, *S.P.E. Trans.*, 1961, 1, 57.
61. E. Rushton, British Electrical and Allied Industries Research Association, *Technical Report* L/T377, 1958; H. Sasakura, *Japan J Appl. Phys.*, 1963, 2, 66.
62. A. Chapiro, "Radiation Chemistry of Polymeric Systems", Interscience, New York, 1962, p 495 *et seq.*
63. S. H. Pinner, *Rep. Progr. Appl. Chem.*, 1958, 43, 463.
64. S. H. Pinner, unpublished work.
65. Raychem U.K., *Technical Bulletin*, RU-203-5, RU-205-2.
66. Union Carbide, *Kabelitems*, No. 126, July, 1963.
67. Gen. Electric Co., Brit. Pat. 831914, 1960.

CHAPTER 8

The Economic Potential for Weather-resistant Plastics

by W. G. SIMPSON

ALTHOUGH STATISTICS for the consumption of plastics materials in various industries are almost completely lacking, it is evident that the tonnage of plastics at present being made into articles for continuous use out-of-doors is comparatively small in comparison with those of such traditional materials as steel and wood. Nevertheless, the use of these materials involves the country in a tremendous annual cost, estimated at about £600 million, in combating the effects of weathering and corrosion. It is, evident, therefore, that there is a very large potential market for plastics in out-of-door applications, provided their weathering properties can be significantly improved.

In considering the possible applications of plastics, it is important to appreciate that these materials can serve in two ways, one as a material in its own right and the other as a means of protecting other materials, and particularly steel, against corrosion by weathering. That the potential for both applications is great is shown by an analysis published a few years ago[1] which places the total sum expended annually in corrosion-preventing measures at over £350 million and gave as a not unreasonable estimate for the cost of wastage and replacement, a figure of some £250 million annually.

The cost of corrosion of steel is a particularly important item in the above assessment of costs. It has been estimated[2] that the total surface of new steel alone which is exposed each year to corrosion attack amounts to 20,000 million square feet and that the annual cost of protecting steel by painting is about £100 million. In addition, galvanizing costs about £35 million, tinning about £10 million and other protective processes about £55 million, making the total cost of protecting steel something like £200 million, or

about one-third of the total annual cost of all forms of corrosion.
Uses of plastics which involve weathering can be divided into
three main types:
  (*i*) in exterior uses in the building industry
  (*ii*) in other products exposed out-of-doors continuously
  (*iii*) in products exposed out-of-doors occasionally.

Plastics in the Building Industry

The construction industry is very large, the value of its output
in 1962 being £3,011 million, compared with £2,854 million in
1961, and the figure has been increasing for many years. The
British Index of Constructional Output, with 1958 as the base year,
rose from 95 in 1954 to 119 seven years later[3]. An impression of its
importance in terms of materials can be obtained from Table 10
which gives the money value of sales of some of the most important
types of materials[4] in the base year, 1958. In addition to these, the
production census classified more than fifty other materials, each
of which had sales valued at less than £10 million in 1958. The total
value of materials consumed in building and construction in that
year would therefore be about £450 million.

TABLE 10. MONEY VALUE OF SALES OF THE MOST IMPORTANT TYPES OF
BUILDING MATERIALS IN 1958.

Material	Sales
Portland cement	£55·2 million
Board, other than coated or laminated	£41·0 million
Stone and slate quarrying	£26·7 million
Plain sheet window glass	£25·1 million
Fletton bricks	£21·4 million
Iron and steel door and window frames	£13·8 million
Sand and gravel	£13·1 million
Wooden doors	£10·1 million

In so far as articles made from plastics and used in building
are concerned, a compilation made in 1961 by the British Plastics
Federation gave the annual consumption figures in Table 11.

TABLE 11. ANNUAL CONSUMPTION OF PLASTIC BUILDING MATERIALS.

Plastics Building Materials	Estimated Consumption in Britain
Rigid polyvinylchloride rainwater and soil pipes	2,000 tons/year
Rigid polyvinylchloride water pipes	700 tons/year
Polyvinylchloride electrical conduit	10 tons/year
Polyvinylchloride ventilation ducting	40 tons/year
Polyethylene pipes and waste fittings	4,000 tons/year
Polyethylene film damp-proof membranes	100 tons/year
Reinforced plastics rooflights and domes	3,000 tons/year
Polymethylmethacrylate rooflights and domes	700 tons/year
Polymethylmethacrylate baths and sinks	200 tons/year
Reinforced plastics roofing sheets	5,350 tons/year

By no means all of the various types of building materials to which reference has been made above would be used externally in such a way as to be exposed to weathering. Normally, only metal or timber products which are exposed out-of-doors are given a standard form of protection against weathering. These products include aluminium door and window frames, glazing bars and aluminium sheets, board (mainly timber in one form or another), building softwood, corrugated galvanized steel sheets, flat galvanized steel sheets, iron and steel door and window frames, metal and wooden doors, fences, gates, hurdles and window frames.

The total annual protection of these particular building materials which are exposed to weathering[5] would appear to be about £70 million.

Judging from the British Plastics Federation's estimates, about 12,000 tons of articles made from plastics go into external uses in the building industry. At an average selling price of £675 per ton, the use of plastics in this connection represents sales worth an annual figure of £8 million. Plastics are therefore comparatively minor building materials at the present time, even when compared with the fairly sophisticated components and fittings referred to above. Glass fibre reinforced polyester sheets are by far the most important products, but the use of rigid polyvinylchloride pipes, guttering and extruded sheet is expected to grow vigorously[6].

TABLE 12. ANNUAL PRODUCTION OF SOME BUILDING MATERIALS WITH
ROUGH EQUIVALENTS IN RIGID POLYVINYLCHLORIDE.

Building Material	Production 1962 (thousand tons)	Rough Equivalent in Rigid Polyvinylchloride (thousand tons)
Asbestos cement sheets		
Corrugated	380 }	60
Flat	52 }	
Corrugated steel sheets	109*	20
Cast-iron pipes and fittings	132	25
* Production in 1958.		

These plastic products can be used in place of a number of traditional materials, but as Table 12 shows, a direct comparison can be made with asbestos-cement sheets, with corrugated steel sheets and with cast-iron pipes and fittings[7]. The rough equivalents, calculated in terms of rigid polyvinylchloride, provide some guide to the potential markets for plastics sheet and pipe as substitutes in traditional applications. There is no possibility of their superseding asbestos-cement and corrugated steel at present price levels, but the calculated tonnages are of particular interest when it is remembered that the total annual production of plastics materials in Britain is only about 650 thousand tons, and that total production of polyvinylchloride of all types[8] (including flexible sheet) is only a little over 100 thousand tons.

In the main, rigid polyvinylchloride sheets and pipes are intended for uses in building which are already traditional in character—they enlarge the range of materials which is available for the well established domestic and industrial forms of construction. Other potentially important uses for plastics in building are more novel.

Reference has been made already to the use of plastics materials as a form of protection for building materials (especially materials such as steel and timber) which are damaged fairly rapidly by weathering. This field is obviously a substantial one, as can be seen from the fact that sales[9] by British manufacturers of paint, one of the most important means of protection against weathering, were worth more than £150 million in 1962.

Steel sheet coated with flexible polyvinylchloride is available and has attracted attention, especially as a facing material for the external walls of large office buildings and for similar contract work. Estimates quoted earlier in this chapter suggested that of the £350 million spent annually on means of protection against corrosion, £200 million was for the protection of steel. Less than one-sixth of all finished steel is used in building[10], but even this fraction of the expenditure is still substantial.

There is a great variety of obstacles to the increased use of plastics materials in the building industry[11], including the traditionalist attitudes and methods of the building industry and also, in many cases, by-law requirements which are integrated with these attitudes and methods. However, two key difficulties have still to be overcome by the plastics manufacturers themselves. These difficulties may be stated as follows:

1. The initial costs of many plastics materials are higher than those of materials with which builders are more familiar. It is likely that these costs can be more than recovered by savings resulting from the use of articles fabricated from plastics—especially, for example, savings in site work. However, reliable cost comparisons are lacking at present.

2. Architects and builders are uncertain about the weatherability of plastics materials, especially when used externally in the form of films or sheets. Many of them would like assurances in terms of hundreds of years, notwithstanding the fact that a typical paint film would expire in five years or less. Really good resistance to weathering would cer-

tainly reduce maintenance costs and, it is to be hoped, would remove altogether the risk of costs as a result of failures. An estimate of the life of a material is needed when calculating annual depreciation charges, and these, together with interest on capital and other running costs (including maintenance labour, materials, overheads, and the cost of downtime) provide the basis for comparative costing of materials in respect of resistance to weathering.

There is need, therefore, for improvements in the weathering properties of plastics, for more precise information about their resistance to weathering, and also for more advanced cost studies.

From the figures already quoted, it will be appreciated that attractive possibilities for plastics of reasonable cost and with good weathering properties exist in the building industry as it is at present constituted and it is important to bear in mind that the organization and methods of the industry may change rapidly during the next ten years. The industry has a fair record of progress, but there are indications that it is not equal to the demands which will be made on it in the future. Signs of strain have been evident during the short bursts of economic growth which have been a feature of the past few years and temporary shortage of resources, such as labour and material, have led in turn to longer completion times[12].

The industry has experienced difficulty in completing annually the 300,000 houses and flats which were set as a target more than ten years ago. In both 1958 and 1959, completions fell short of the target and completions in 1962 were only 315,000, compared with 327,000 nine years previously[13]. On the other hand, it has been stated that a target of 450,000 completions annually would be related more closely to current requirements. Incidentally, this figure has regard to both the continuing shortage of accommodation and the need to replace old dwellings[14]. Increased demand for constructional work on the part of public authorities is also likely, especially for such buildings as hospitals and schools. Britain has many whole towns which are obsolete and which ought to be rebuilt. Projects of this order are clearly beyond the scope of the construction industry in Britain as it is at present constituted.

A recent report on the industry[15] commented:

"The average level of building output over the next ten years is likely to be between £3,750 million and £4,300 million (at constant 1961 prices), or between 30 and 50 per cent above the 1961 level—discounting short term fluctuations.

"The basic problems for the building industry are, therefore: to increase its output with a virtually static labour force; to meet the demand for improved standards of accommodation and amenity; and, at the same time, to avoid increasing—and, if possible, to reduce—the price of its finished products . . . when land values, material costs and wages are rising".

Government authority has been given to efforts to persuade the construction industry to prepare itself to meet these problems. Emphasis has been placed upon industrialized methods of building which will help to raise the level of productivity. Plastics could play an important part in the development of such methods, since they are man-made materials for which quality control can be fairly rigid, and because they offer unique properties, especially high strength-weight ratios and resistance to corrosion.

In addition to improved forms of existing plastics materials, it is possible that new types will play a significant part in markets such as these. One such group of materials are the polyvinyl-fluoride films, which have recently been introduced commercially. These films are intended for use as weather-resistant facings for metal sheets and boards of various types, and they are a superior form of protection for which an exceptionally long service life is anticipated[16]. The possibilities for sales of these films as facings for curtain wall infill panels do not seem particularly impressive at the present time, but annual sales of tens of millions of square feet could be anticipated as facings for industrial building components. Their use as a weather protection outside the building industry could also be important.

Other Products Exposed Continuously Out-of-doors

Much of what has been said about the use of plastics materials out-of-doors in the building industry also applies to the great variety of outdoor uses which are open to them in other fields. It is impossible to compile a complete list of these uses, but among the main ones, reference may be made to advertising signs, agricultural machinery parts, caravan coachwork, chemical plant (such as storage tanks and pipework), contractor's equipment components (crane cabs, motor covers, etc.), commercial vehicle components (cab or trailer panelling), garden furniture, rick covers and other farm uses (such as reservoir linings), motor vehicle and cycle parts, railway rolling stock (panels or smaller components), road signs and signals, ships and boats (fittings, or hulls in the case of small craft) and vending and dispensing machines.

As in building, plastics are already used to some extent in each of these fields, their many advantages (ease of fabrication, resistance to corrosion, attractive appearance, and so on) having resulted in wide interest. Once again, the main drawbacks are high initial costs compared with metals, timber and ceramics, and uncertainty with regard to weathering properties.

There are, however, a number of ways in which the uses listed above differ from uses for plastics in the building industry. The principal markets in the building industry can be satisfied by a comparatively narrow range of basic materials—polymethylmethacrylate, glass-reinforced polyester, and polyvinylchloride—mainly in sheet form or as extrusions, but the various other outdoor uses call for a much wider range of materials in various fabricated forms, including mouldings. They, therefore, widen the range of materials for which reasonable weathering properties are required, and also the range of colours, surface finishes and fabrication qualities which may be needed.

Without considering in detail all the various markets referred to above, a few examples will show their potential importance.

Expenditure on outdoor illuminated advertising signs[17] was £14·5 million in 1962, about £2 million of which was for materials. Total expenditure on all forms of outdoor advertising was £30·7 million. There is obviously scope in this field for substantial sales of sheet materials, such as polymethylmethacrylate, cellulose acetate butyrate, and rigid polyvinylchloride.

Production of agricultural machinery other than tractors[18] is valued at about £170 million annually. Weatherable plastics could only have a minor role in such machines—as panel materials and small mouldings—but it could nevertheless be of significant value. Similar comments apply to components for contractor's equipment, commercial vehicles and railway rolling stock. For satisfactory plastics components, a market in these trades worth £10 million annually does not seem at all unreasonable.

The possibilities in fields such as caravans, garden furniture and vending machines are much smaller, but not insignificant. The forthcoming rationalization of Britain's 1,500,000 road signs will bring a very large, if temporary, increase in the consumption of sign materials.

The motor industry is already a very important user of plastics materials and it is not inconceivable that plastics with good weathering properties could be used extensively, not only as small parts for emblems and light fittings, but for grilles, fenders, and other exterior features. Plastics-coated steel sheet might be of particular interest here.

These miscellaneous uses are of more immediate interest to specialist fabricators of plastics than to plastics material manufacturers themselves, and there would appear to be excellent opportunities for enterprise of this type. One can only guess at the total tonnage of materials which could be involved, since detailed studies would be needed for each type of use. A few tens of thousands of tons seems to be in the right range, and this might be of above-average value to the industry as a whole, since there would be a higher charge for fabrication than in the case of plastics sheets for use in building.

Products with Occasional Outdoor Use

In conclusion, a brief reference should be made to the class of articles which are exposed out-of-doors occasionally. Some objects, such as portable radios and children's toys, spend more time out-of-doors than others, but almost any article made from plastics is liable to spend some time in the open, either during a move from one place to another, or because it is needed on a picnic or a trip. For the most part, materials stand up perfectly well to occasional exposure and this is a characteristic of manufacturing materials that every user has the right to expect. However, improvements intended primarily for products used out-of-doors continuously can also, in the long run, benefit every type of material, and thus contribute to the steady development of plastics in all their many uses.

REFERENCES

1. W. H. J. Vernon, *Chem. and Ind.*, 1958, 1387.
2. J. C. Hudson, *Chem. and Ind.*, 1960, 363-4.
3. *Annual Abstract of Statistics*, 1962, Tables 195 and 155.
   Monthly Digest of Statistics, Table 102.
4. *The Building Industry*—1962 onwards. A survey 1962, 122, Table 3 (b)
   (*The Builder*).
5. *Ibid.*
6. E. A. O. Mange, *British Plastics Federation Conference Papers*, 1962, 20.
7. *Monthly Digest of Statistics*, Table 107.
   The Report on the Census of Production, 1958, Part 38.
8. *Business Monitor: Production series*, Part 21 (Board of Trade).
9. *Ibid.*, Part 18.
10. *Iron and Steel Annual Statistics*, 1962, Table 65 (Iron and Steel Board and the British Iron and Steel Federation).
11. F. M. Lea, *Chem. and Ind.*, 1962, 1840-46.
12. G. Cyriax, *Financial Times*, 3/7/63, 12, and 4/7/63, 10.
13. *Annual Abstract of Statistics*, 1962, Table 59.
    Monthly Digest of Statistics, Table 104.
14. J. Greve, *The Housing Problem*, Fabian Research series 224.
    (The Fabian Society, 1961).
15. The Builder Survey (reference 4 above), 1962, 22.
16. V. L. Simril and B. A. Curry, *Modern Plastics*, 1959, 36 (11), 121.
17. Advertising Association figures.
18. *Monthly Digest of Statistics*, Table 69.

Index

Edited by S. H. Pinner
Borough Polytechnic
London

This book is based on a symposium organized for broader dissemination, in an illustrated and fully documented form, of the factors resulting in the degradation of polymers under the influence of heat, visible and high energy radiation, oxidation, hydrolysis, etc.

Contents